PEARSON

EARNING

Lillian C. McDermott • Peter S. Shaffer

Tutorials in Introductory Physics

Second Custom Edition for University of Colorado at Boulder

Taken from:
Tutorials in Introductory Physics
by Lillian C. McDermott, Peter S. Shaffer, and the Physics Education Group

Taken from:
Tutorials in Introductory Physics
by Lillian C. McDermott, Peter S. Shaffer and the Physics Education Group
Copyright © 2002 by Pearson Education, Inc.
Published by Prentice-Hall
Upper Saddle River, New Jersey 07458

Pearson Learning Solutions, 501 Boylston Street, Suite 900, Boston, MA 02116
A Pearson Education Company
www.pearsoned.com

Printed in the United States of America

5 6 7 8 9 10 V0ZN 17 16 15 14

000200010271767660

CT

ISBN 10: 1-269-32006-8
ISBN 13: 978-1-269-32006-1

Preface

Tutorials in Introductory Physics is a set of instructional materials intended to supplement the lectures and textbook of a standard introductory physics course. The emphasis in the tutorials is on the development of important physical concepts and scientific reasoning skills, not on solving the standard quantitative problems found in traditional textbooks.

There is increasing evidence that after instruction in a typical course, many students are unable to apply the physics formalism that they have studied to situations that they have not expressly memorized. In order for meaningful learning to occur, students need more assistance than they can obtain through listening to lectures, reading the textbook, and solving standard quantitative problems. It can be difficult for students who are studying physics for the first time to recognize what they do and do not understand and to learn to ask themselves the types of questions necessary to come to a functional understanding of the material. *Tutorials in Introductory Physics* provides a structure that promotes the active mental engagement of students in the process of learning physics. Questions in the tutorials guide students through the reasoning necessary to construct concepts and to apply them in real-world situations. The tutorials also provide practice in interpreting scientific representations (*e.g.*, verbal descriptions, diagrams, graphs, and formulas) and in translating back and forth among them. For the most part, the tutorials are intended to be used after concepts have been introduced in the lectures and the laboratory, although many can serve to introduce the topic as well.

The tutorials comprise an integrated system of pretests, worksheets, homework assignments, and post-tests. (The student materials consist of the tutorial worksheets and homework assignments.) The tutorial sequence begins with a pretest, which is usually on material already presented in lecture or textbook but not yet covered in tutorial. The pretests help students identify what they do and not understand about the material and what they are expected to learn in the upcoming tutorial. They also inform the instructors about the level of student understanding. The worksheets, which consist of carefully sequenced tasks and questions, provide the structure for the tutorial sessions. Students work together in small groups, constructing answers for themselves through discussions with one another and with the tutorial instructors. The tutorial instructors do not lecture but ask questions designed to help students find their own answers. The tutorial homework reinforces and extends what is covered in the worksheets. For the tutorials to be most effective, it is important that the tutorial instructors be well-prepared and that course examinations include questions that emphasize the concepts and reasoning skills developed in the tutorials.

The tutorials have been developed through an iterative cycle of research on the learning and teaching of physics, design of curriculum based on this research, and assessment through rigorous pretesting and post-testing in the classroom. *Tutorials in Introductory Physics* has been developed and tested at the University of Washington and pilot-tested at other colleges and universities.

These instructional materials are primarily designed for a small class setting but have proved to be adaptable to other instructional environments. The curriculum has been shown to be effective for students in regular and honors sections of calculus-based and algebra-based physics.

Comments on the Second Edition for the University of Colorado

Ongoing research has led to modifications to the tutorials and associated homework in the Preliminary and First Editions of *Tutorials in Introductory Physics*. This Second Edition, customized for the University of Colorado, incorporates these changes and also includes several new tutorials.

Acknowledgments

Tutorials in Introductory Physics is the product of close collaboration by many members of the Physics Education Group at the University of Washington. Prof. Paula Heron has played an important role in their development. Significant contributions to the First and Second Editions have also been made by current and former graduate students, post-doctoral research associates, and faculty: Bradley Ambrose, Andrew Boudreaux, Hunter Close, Matt Cochran, Julie Crockett, Andrew Crouse, Stephen Kanim, Christian Kautz, Mila Kryjevskaia, Beth Lindsey, Michael Loverude, Luanna G. Ortiz, Mel Sabella, Homeyra Sadaghiani, Rachel Scherr, Mark Somers, MacKenzie Stetzer, John Thompson, Stamatis Vokos, Eleanor Warfield, and Karen Wosilait. Others, whose work on the Preliminary Edition enriched later Editions include: Chris Border, Patricia Chastain, Randal Harrington, Pamela Kraus, Graham Oberem, Tara O'Brien Pride, Daryl Pedigo, Christopher Richardson, and Richard Steinberg. Lezlie S. DeWater and Donna Messina, experienced K-12 teachers, provided many insights and suggestions.

The collaboration of other colleagues in the Physics Department has been invaluable. Faculty in the introductory calculus-based sequence and graduate and undergraduate students who have served as tutorial instructors have made many useful comments. Contributions have also been made by many long-term and short-term visitors to our group. Physics instructors who have pilot-tested the tutorials and have provided valuable feedback over an extended period of time include: John Christopher (University of Kentucky), Romana Crnkovic (Minot State University), William Duxler (Los Angeles Pierce College), Robert Endorf (University of Cincinnati), Gregory Francis (Montana State University), James Freericks and Amy Liu (Georgetown University), Gary Gladding (University of Illinois, Urbana-Champaign), Gregory Kilcup (The Ohio State University), Heidi Mauk (The United States Air Force Academy), Eric Mazur (Harvard University), Steven Pollock and Noah Finkelstein (University of Colorado, Boulder), James Poth (Miami University), and E.F. Redish (University of Maryland).

We thank former editors, Alison Reeves and Erik Fahlgren for their encouragement and advice. We also gratefully acknowledge the support of the National Science Foundation, which has enabled the Physics Education Group to conduct the ongoing, comprehensive program of research, curriculum development, and instruction that has produced *Tutorials in Introductory Physics*. The tutorials have also benefited from the concurrent development of *Physics by Inquiry* (©1996 John Wiley & Sons, Inc.). *Tutorials in Introductory Physics* and *Physics by Inquiry* share a common research base and portions of each have been adapted for the other.

Table of Contents

Part I: Mechanics

Kinematics

Newton's laws

Energy and momentum

Rotation and harmonic motion

Part II: Electricity and magnetism

Electrostatics

Electric circuits

Magnetism

Electromagnetism

Part III: Waves

Part IV: Optics

Geometrical optics

Physical optics

Part V: Selected topics

Mechanics

I. Motion with constant speed

Each person in your group should obtain a ruler and at least one ticker tape segment from the staff. All the tape segments were generated using the same ticker timer. Do not write on or fold the tapes. If a ticker timer is available, examine it so that you are familiar with how it works.

A. Describe the motion represented by your segment of tape. Explain your reasoning.

B. Compare your tape segment with those of your partners.

How does the time taken to generate one of the short tape segments compare to the time taken to generate one of the long tape segments? Explain your answer.

Describe how you could use your answer above to arrange the segments in order by speed.

C. Suppose the ticker timer that made the dots strikes the tape every $1/60^{th}$ of a second.

How far did the object that generated your tape segment move in: $1/60^{th}$ of a second? $2/60^{th}$ of a second? $3/60^{th}$ of a second? Explain your answer.

Predict how far the object would move in: 1 second, $1/120^{th}$ of a second. Explain the assumption(s) you used to make your predictions.

D. In your own words, describe a procedure you could use to calculate the speed of an object.

E. Determine the speed of the object that generated each of your tapes. Record your answers below.

Give an interpretation of the speed of the object, *i.e.,* explain the meaning of the number you just calculated. Do not use the word "speed" in your answer. (*Hint:* Which of the distances that you calculated in part C is numerically equal to the speed?)

Write the speed of the object that generated each tape on a small piece of paper and attach the paper to the tape. Express your answer in terms of centimeters and seconds.

F. A motion that generates a sequence of evenly-spaced dots on a ticker tape is called motion with *constant speed*. Explain the assumption about the motion that is being made when this phrase is applied.

Discuss with your partners whether the object that generated your tape was moving with constant velocity.

G. A model train moving with constant velocity travels 60 cm for every 1.5 s that elapses. Answer the questions below and discuss your reasoning with your partners.

1. Is there a name that is commonly given to the quantity represented by the number 40 (40 = 60/1.5)? If so, what is the name?

To denote the quantity completely, what additional information must be given besides the number 40?

How would you *interpret* the number 40 in this instance? (*Note:* A name is *not* an interpretation. Your response should be in terms of centimeters and seconds.)

Use your interpretation (not algebra) to find the distance the train moves in 2.5 s.

2. Is there a name that is commonly given to the quantity represented by the number 0.025 (0.025 = 1.5/60)? If so, what is the name?

How would you *interpret* the number 0.025?

Use your interpretation (not algebra) to find the time it takes the train to move 90 cm.

II. Motion with varying speed

A. In the space below, sketch a possible ticker tape resulting from motion with varying speed and write a description of the motion.

How can you tell from your diagram that the motion has varying speed?

B. Together with your classmates, take your ticker tape segments and arrange yourselves in a line, ranked according to the speed of the segments. Discuss the following questions as a class.

Compare your segment of ticker tape to neighboring tape segments. What do you observe?

Compare the smallest and largest speeds. What do you observe?

C. Based on your observations of your tape segment and the tape segments of other members of your class, answer the following questions.

Is each small tape segment a part of a motion with constant or varying speed?

Did your examination of a single, small tape segment reveal whether the entire motion that generated the tape had constant or varying speed?

D. Review your earlier interpretation of the speed for your small tape segment. (See section I.) Is that interpretation valid for the entire motion that generated the tape?

Based on the speed for your piece of tape, could you successfully predict how far the object would move in: $1/60^{th}$ s? $2/60^{th}$ s? 1 s?

How can you modify the interpretation of the speed so that it applies even to motion with varying speed?

What name is given to a speed that is interpreted in this way?

E. Suppose you selected two widely separated dots on the ticker tape assembled in part B. What would you call the number you would obtain if you divided the distance between the dots by the time it took the object to move between the dots?

How would you interpret this number?

Tutorials in Introductory Physics
McDermott, Shaffer, and the P.E.G., U. Wash.

©Pearson
Custom 2nd Ed., for U.CO, Boulder

In this tutorial, you will use a motion detector to graph your motion and to investigate how motion can be described in terms of position, velocity, and acceleration. See your instructor for instructions on using the equipment.

General tips

When using a motion detector:

- Stay in line with the detector and do not swing your arms. For best results, take off bulky sweaters or other loose-fitting clothing. You may find it helpful to hold a large board in front of you in order to present a larger target for the detector.

- Do not stand closer than about 0.5 meter or farther than 4.0 meters from the detector.

- It is difficult to obtain good a versus t graphs with the motion detector. Discuss any questions about your a versus t graphs with an instructor.

Instructions

In each of the following problems, you will be given one of the following descriptions of a motion:

- a written description, or

- an x versus t, v versus t, or a versus t graph.

Predict the other three descriptions of the motion, then use the motion detector to check your answers. Check your predictions one-by-one, instead of checking several problems at once. In addition, answer the questions posed at the bottom of each page.

Note: So that your graphs emphasize important features, draw them in an idealized form rather than showing many small wiggles.

Example: The problem below has been worked as an example. Use the motion detector to verify the answers.

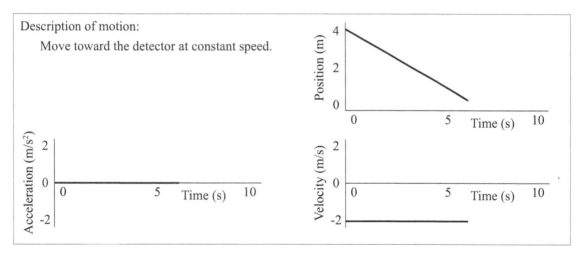

Description of motion:

Move toward the detector at constant speed.

A. The computer program assumes a particular coordinate system. Describe this coordinate system.

Tutorials in Introductory Physics
McDermott, Shaffer, and the P.E.G., U. Wash.

©Pearson
Custom 2nd Ed., for U.CO, Boulder

B.

C.

D.

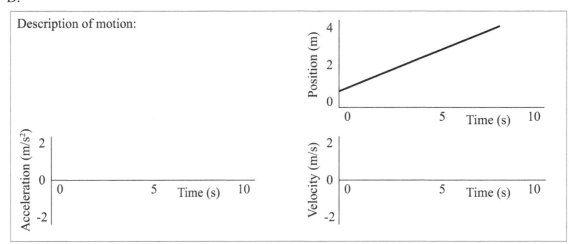

E.   How are the motions in parts C and D similar? How do they differ? How are the graphs similar? How do they differ?

F.

G.

H.

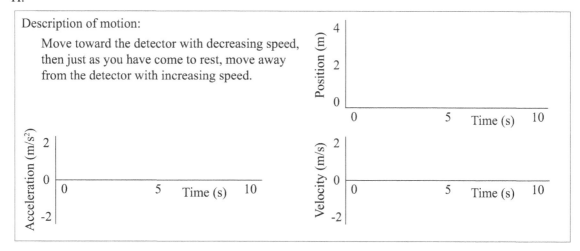

Description of motion:

Move toward the detector with decreasing speed, then just as you have come to rest, move away from the detector with increasing speed.

I.   How do the acceleration graphs for F, G, and H compare? Is it possible to have: a positive acceleration and slow down? a negative acceleration and speed up?

J.

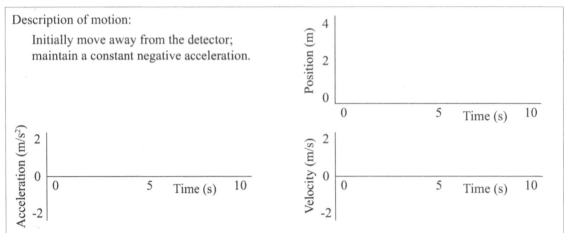

Description of motion:

Initially move away from the detector; maintain a constant negative acceleration.

K.

Description of motion:

L.

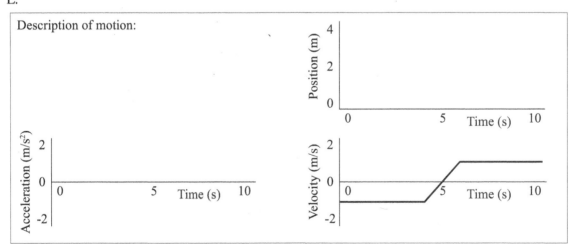

Description of motion:

M. The term *decelerate* is often used to indicate that an object is slowing down. Does this term indicate the sign of the acceleration?

I. Motion with decreasing speed

The diagram below represents a strobe photograph of a ball as it rolls *up* a track. (In a strobe photograph, the position of an object is shown at instants separated by *equal time intervals*.)

Turnaround point

A. Draw vectors on your diagram that represent the instantaneous velocity of the ball at each of the instants shown. If the magnitude of the velocity is zero at any instant, indicate that explicitly. Explain why you drew the vectors as you did.

We will call diagrams like the one you drew above *velocity diagrams*. Unless otherwise specified, a velocity diagram shows both the location and the velocity of an object at instants in time that are separated by equal time intervals.

B. In the space at right, compare the velocities at instants *1* and *2* by sketching the vectors that represent those velocities. Draw the vectors side-by-side and label them $\vec{v}_1$ and $\vec{v}_2$, respectively.

Draw the vector that must be *added* to the velocity at the earlier time to equal the velocity at the later time. Label this vector $\Delta\vec{v}$.

$\vec{v}_1, \vec{v}_2,$ and $\Delta\vec{v}$

Why is the name *change in velocity* appropriate for this vector?

How does the direction of the change in velocity vector compare to the direction of the velocity vectors?

Would your answer differ if you were to select two *different* consecutive instants (*e.g.*, instants *3* and *4*) while the ball was slowing down? Explain.

Tutorials in Introductory Physics
McDermott, Shaffer, and the P.E.G., U. Wash.

©Pearson
Custom 2nd Ed., for U.CO, Boulder

How would the magnitude of the change in velocity vector between instants *1* and *2* compare to the magnitude of the change in velocity vector between two *different* consecutive instants *(e.g.,* instants *3* and *4)?* Explain. (You may find it useful to refer to the graph of *velocity* versus *time* for the motion.)

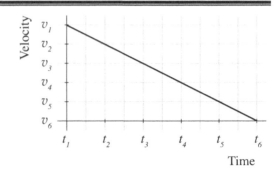

Note: The positive direction has been chosen to be *up* the track.

C. Consider the change in velocity vector between two instants on the velocity diagram that are not consecutive, *e.g.,* instants *1* and *4.*

Is the direction of the change in velocity vector different than it was for consecutive instants? Explain.

Is the length of the change in velocity vector different than it was for consecutive instants? If so, how many times larger or smaller is it than the corresponding vector for consecutive instants? Explain.

D. Use the definition of acceleration to draw a vector in the space at right that represents the acceleration of the ball between instants *1* and *2.*

Acceleration vector

How is the direction of the acceleration vector related to the direction of the change in velocity vector? Explain.

E. Does the acceleration change as the ball rolls up the track? Would the acceleration vector you obtain differ if you were to choose (1) two different successive instants on your diagram or (2) two instants that are not consecutive? Explain.

F. Generalize your results thus far to answer the following question:

What is the relationship between the direction of the acceleration and the direction of the velocity for an object that is moving in a straight line and slowing down? Explain.

Describe the direction of the acceleration of a ball that is rolling up a straight incline.

II. Motion with increasing speed

The diagram below represents a strobe photograph of a ball as it rolls *down* the track.

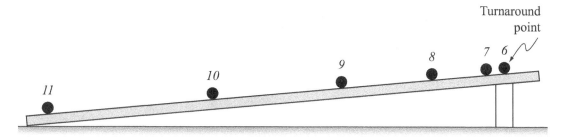

A. Choose two successive instants. In the space at right, sketch the velocity vectors corresponding to those instants. Draw the vectors side-by-side and label them $\vec{v}_i$ and $\vec{v}_f$, respectively.

Determine the vector that must be added to the velocity at the earlier time to equal the velocity at the later time. Is the name *change in velocity* appropriate for this vector?

$\vec{v}_i, \vec{v}_f$, and $\Delta\vec{v}$

How does the direction of the change in velocity vector compare to the direction of the velocity vectors in this case?

Would your answer differ if you were to select two *different* instants during the time that the ball was speeding up? Explain.

B. In the space at right, draw a vector to represent the acceleration of the ball between the instants chosen above.

Acceleration vector

How is the direction of the change in velocity vector related to the direction of the acceleration vector? Explain.

Generalize your results thus far to answer the following question:

What is the relationship between the direction of the acceleration and the direction of the velocity for an object that is moving in a straight line and speeding up? Explain.

Describe the direction of the acceleration of a ball that is rolling down a straight incline.

III. Motion that includes a change in direction

A. Complete the velocity diagram below for the portion of the motion that includes the turnaround.

B. Choose an instant *before* the turnaround and another *after*.

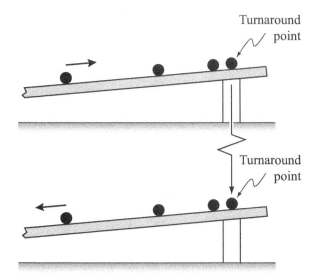

In the space below, draw the velocity vectors and label them $\vec{v}_i$ and $\vec{v}_f$.

Draw the vector that must be added to the velocity at the earlier time to obtain the velocity at the later time.

Is the name *change in velocity* that you used in sections I and II also appropriate for this vector?

C. Suppose that you had chosen the turnaround as one of your instants.

What is the velocity at the turnaround point?

Would this choice affect the direction of the change in velocity vector? Explain why or why not.

$\vec{v}_i$, $\vec{v}_f$, and $\Delta\vec{v}$

D. In the space at right, draw a vector that represents the acceleration of the ball between the instants you chose in part C above.

Compare the direction of the acceleration of the ball at the turnaround point to that of the ball as it rolls: (1) up the track and (2) down the track.

Acceleration vector

Tutorials in Introductory Physics
McDermott, Shaffer, and the P.E.G., U. Wash.

©Pearson
Custom 2nd Ed., for U.CO, Boulder

I. Velocity

An object is moving around an oval track as shown at right. Sketch the trajectory on a large sheet of paper. (Make your diagram *large*.) Point O is the origin of the coordinate system.

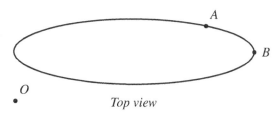

Top view

A. Draw $\vec{r}_A$ and $\vec{r}_B$, the position vectors for the object when it is at points A and B.

B. Draw the vector that represents the displacement of the object (*i.e.*, the change in position) from A to B.

Describe how to use the displacement vector to determine the direction of the average velocity of the object between A and B. Draw a vector to represent the average velocity.

C. Choose a point on the oval between points A and B, and label that point B'.

As point B' is chosen to lie closer and closer to point A, does the direction of the average velocity over the interval AB' change? If so, how?

What happens to the magnitude of the displacement as point B' is chosen to lie closer and closer to point A? Does this magnitude approach a limiting value? If so, what is that value?

Must the magnitude of the average velocity change in the same way? Explain.

D. Describe the direction of the (instantaneous) velocity of the object at point A.

How would you characterize the direction of the (instantaneous) velocity at *any* point on the trajectory?

II. Acceleration for motion with constant speed

Suppose that the object in section I is moving around the track at *constant speed*.

A. On your large diagram, draw vectors to represent the velocities at points A and B.

Tutorials in Introductory Physics
McDermott, Shaffer, and the P.E.G., U. Wash.

©Pearson
Custom 2nd Ed., for U.CO, Boulder

1. Did the *speed* of the object change? Explain how you can tell from the vectors that you have drawn.

2. Did the *velocity* of the object change? Explain how you can tell from the vectors that you have drawn.

B. On a *separate* part of your paper, copy the velocity vectors $\vec{v}_A$ and $\vec{v}_B$ so that their "tails" are at the same point.

> $\vec{v}_A$, $\vec{v}_B$, and $\Delta\vec{v}$

   1. From your diagram, determine the *change in velocity vector, $\Delta\vec{v}$.*

   2. Describe how to use the change in velocity vector to determine the direction of the average acceleration of the object between A and B. Draw a vector to represent the average acceleration between points A and B.

   3. On your diagram, label the angle θ between the "head" of $\vec{v}_A$ and the "tail" of $\Delta\vec{v}$. Is this angle *greater than*, *less than*, or *equal to* 90°? Explain your reasoning.

As point B is chosen to lie closer and closer to point A, does the angle θ *increase*, *decrease*, or *remain the same?* Explain how you can tell.

Does the angle θ approach a *limiting* value? If so, what is that value?

   4. As point B is chosen to lie closer and closer to point A, the magnitude of $\Delta\vec{v}$ approaches zero. Does the magnitude of the average acceleration also approach zero? Explain.

   5. Determine the direction of the (instantaneous) acceleration at point A.

Tutorials in Introductory Physics
McDermott, Shaffer, and the P.E.G., U. Wash.

©Pearson
Custom 2nd Ed., for U.CO, Boulder

Draw a diagram that shows the velocity and acceleration at point *A*. Place both vectors with their tails at point *A*. Is the angle between the acceleration and the velocity *greater than, less than,* or *equal to* 90°?

⇨ Check your reasoning for part B with a tutorial instructor.

C. Suppose you were to choose a new point on the trajectory where the *curvature is greater than* at point *A (e.g.,* point *B).*

   1. Is the magnitude of the acceleration at the new point *greater than, less than,* or *equal to* the magnitude of the acceleration at point *A?* Explain your reasoning.

   2. Describe the direction of the acceleration at the new point.

   3. At each of the indicated points on the diagram at right, sketch a vector that represents the acceleration of the object.

     Is the acceleration directed toward the "center" of the oval at every point on the trajectory?

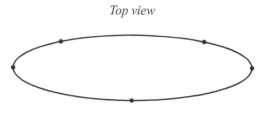

Top view

Acceleration vectors for constant speed

D. Suppose that the object had been moving faster (*e.g.,* twice as fast), but still uniformly.

Would the magnitude of the acceleration at a particular point (*e.g.,* point *A*) be *greater than, less than,* or *equal to* that when the object was moving more slowly? Draw a diagram to support your answer.

E. Summarize your results from parts C and D above in a rule for comparing the magnitudes of the accelerations of two objects when:

• the speeds of the two objects are the same but the curvatures of the paths are different

• the curvatures of the paths are the same but the speeds of the two objects are different

⇨ Discuss parts C–E with a tutorial instructor.

III. Acceleration for motion with increasing speed

Suppose that the object is *speeding up* as it moves around the oval track. Draw vectors to represent the velocity at two points on the track that are relatively close together. Label the two points C and D.

A. On a *separate* part of your paper, copy the velocity vectors $\vec{v}_C$ and $\vec{v}_D$ so that they are tail-to-tail. Use the same procedure as in previous sections to determine the change in velocity, $\Delta\vec{v}$.

1. Label the angle θ between the head of $\vec{v}_C$ and the tail of $\Delta\vec{v}$. Is this angle *greater than, less than,* or *equal to* 90°?

2. Determine the direction of the average acceleration of the object between C and D.

3. Describe how you could use a limiting process to determine the direction of the acceleration of the object at point C.

Consider the acceleration at point C. Is the angle between the acceleration and the velocity (placed tail-to-tail) *greater than, less than,* or *equal to* 90°?

4. Two students consider how θ changes as point D is chosen to lie closer and closer to point C.

   Velocity vectors

   Student 1: "The object is speeding up and moving on a curve, so $\vec{v}_C$ and $\vec{v}_D$ differ in both magnitude and direction. However, as point D gets close to C, they eventually have the same magnitude like I've drawn. So, in the limit, the angle between the head of $\vec{v}_C$ and the tail of $\Delta\vec{v}$ is 90°—the same as for constant speed."

   Student 1:
   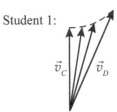

   Student 2: "I agree that both the magnitudes and directions of the velocity vectors are different. But I think that eventually the interval gets small enough that the direction of the average acceleration doesn't change, like for the vectors I've drawn. So the angle between the head of $\vec{v}_C$ and the tail of $\Delta\vec{v}$ approaches a limiting value that is greater than 90°."

   Student 2:

   With which student, if either, do you agree? Explain your reasoning.

5. In light of your answer to part 4, reconsider your answer to part 3. If necessary, modify your answer to part 3.

Tutorials in Introductory Physics
McDermott, Shaffer, and the P.E.G., U. Wash.

©Pearson
Custom 2nd Ed., for U.CO, Boulder

I. Position and displacement relative to different observers

Two spaceships, A and B, move toward one another as shown. At time t_i, spaceship A launches a shuttle craft toward spaceship B. At time t_f, the shuttle reaches spaceship B.

A. The second diagram at right shows the positions of spaceships A, B, and the shuttle at time t_i in the reference frame of spaceship B.

Diagram for reference frame of spaceship B

Sketch spaceship A and the shuttle at their positions at time t_f *as measured in the reference frame of spaceship B.*

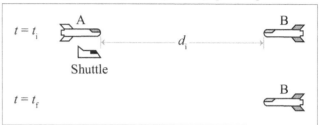

Explain how the diagram is consistent with the fact that in its own frame of reference, spaceship B is not moving.

In the box at right, draw and label vectors for the following quantities:

$\vec{x}_{Si}$, $\vec{x}_{Sf}$, and $\Delta\vec{x}_S$ in frame of spaceship B

- $\vec{x}_{Si}^{(B)}$ (the *initial position* of the shuttle in the frame of spaceship B)

- $\vec{x}_{Sf}^{(B)}$ (the *final position* of the shuttle in the frame of spaceship B)

- $\Delta\vec{x}_S^{(B)}$ (the *displacement,* or *change in position,* of the shuttle in the frame of spaceship B).

Is the quantity $\Delta\vec{x}_S^{(B)}$ associated with:
- a single instant in time or an interval of time? Explain.

- the distance between two objects or the distance traveled by a single object? Explain.

Describe how you could use $\Delta\vec{x}_S^{(B)}$ to determine the velocity of the shuttle in the frame of spaceship B.

Tutorials in Introductory Physics
McDermott, Shaffer, and the P.E.G., U. Wash.

©Pearson
Custom 2nd Ed., for U.CO, Boulder

B. The picture of the spaceships and shuttle from the previous page is reproduced at right.

The diagram below the picture shows the positions of the two spaceships and the shuttle at time t_i in the reference frame of spaceship A.

Diagram for reference frame of spaceship A

Sketch spaceship A, B, and the shuttle at their positions at time t_f *as measured in the reference frame of spaceship A*.

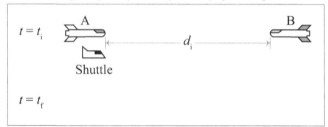

In the box at right, draw and label vectors for $\vec{x}_{Si}^{(A)}$, $\vec{x}_{Sf}^{(A)}$, and $\Delta\vec{x}_S^{(A)}$.

$\vec{x}_{Si}$, $\vec{x}_{Sf}$, and $\Delta\vec{x}_S$ in frame of spaceship A

Describe how you could use $\Delta\vec{x}_S^{(A)}$ to determine the velocity of the shuttle in the frame of spaceship A.

Is the magnitude of the velocity of the shuttle in the frame of spaceship A *greater than, less than,* or *equal to* the magnitude of the velocity of the shuttle in the frame of spaceship B? Explain.

C. Rank d_i, d_f, $|\Delta\vec{x}_S^{(A)}|$, and $|\Delta\vec{x}_S^{(B)}|$, from largest to smallest. Make sure that your ranking is consistent with your previous results.

Tutorials in Introductory Physics
McDermott, Shaffer, and the P.E.G., U. Wash.

©Pearson
Custom 2ⁿᵈ Ed., for U.CO, Boulder

D. Spaceship C moves so as to remain a fixed distance behind spaceship B at all times.

Diagram for reference frame of spaceship C

The diagram at right shows the positions of the three spaceships and the shuttle at time t_i in the reference frame of spaceship C.

On the diagram show the positions of the spaceships and the shuttle at time t_f *as measured in the reference frame of spaceship C.*

In the box at right, draw and label vectors for $\vec{x}_{Si}{}^{(C)}$, $\vec{x}_{Sf}{}^{(C)}$, and $\Delta\vec{x}_S{}^{(C)}$.

$\vec{x}_{Si}$, $\vec{x}_{Sf}$, and $\Delta\vec{x}_S$ in frame of spaceship C

Is the magnitude of the displacement of the shuttle in the frame of spaceship C *greater than, less than,* or *equal to* the magnitude of the displacement of the shuttle in the frame of spaceship B? Explain.

E. Consider the following statement:

"The displacement of the shuttle is greater relative to spaceship C than it is relative to spaceship B. At time t_f, the shuttle is right next to spaceship B, but it is still a large distance away from spaceship C."

Do you agree or disagree? Explain.

If all displacements of an object (such as the shuttle) are measured to have the same value by two different observers, those observers are said to be *in the same frame of reference.*

F. State which of the spaceships, if any, are in the same frame of reference. Explain.

Generalize your answer to describe the conditions under which two observers are in the same frame of reference.

II. Relative velocity

A car and a truck move on a straight road. Their positions are shown at instants *1–3*, separated by equal time intervals.

A. Describe the motion of the car and the truck (*i.e.,* the direction of motion of each object and whether it is speeding up, slowing down, or moving with constant speed).

B. Complete the diagram at right by drawing the car and the truck at their positions at instants *2* and *3 as measured in the reference frame of the truck.*

Explain how your completed diagram is consistent with the fact that the truck is at rest in its own frame of reference.

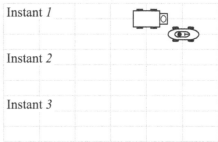

Diagram for the reference frame of the truck

Instant *1*

Instant *2*

Instant *3*

Tutorials in Introductory Physics
McDermott, Shaffer, and the P.E.G., U. Wash.

©Pearson
Custom 2nd Ed., for U.CO, Boulder

C. Use your completed diagram to sketch average velocity vectors for the car *in the reference frame of the truck* for the intervals indicated.

In the reference frame of the truck:

Average velocity of car
in frame of truck

- is the car moving to the *east, moving to the west,* or *at rest?*
  Explain.

from *1* to *2* ▭

from *2* to *3* ▭

- is the car speeding up, slowing down, or moving with constant speed? Explain.

D. During a small time interval Δt from just before to just after instant *2*, does the car *move to the east, move to the west,* or *remain at rest* in the reference frame of the truck? Explain.

In the space provided, draw an arrow to indicate the direction of the *instantaneous* velocity vector of the car in the reference frame of the truck at instant *2*. If the velocity is zero, state that explicitly.

Direction of
instantaneous velocity of car
in frame of truck
at instant *2*

▭

Consider the following statements:

Statement 1: "At instant 2 the car and the truck are side by side, so the velocity of the car in the truck's frame is zero at that instant."

Statement 2: "Before instant 2, the truck is catching up to the car, so the truck sees the car as slowing down."

Do you agree or disagree with each of the statements? Explain.

⇨ Discuss your reasoning with an instructor.

I. Identifying forces

Two people are attempting to move a large block. The block, however, does not move. Chris pushes on the block. Pam pulls on a rope attached to the block.

A. Draw a dot on a large sheet of paper to represent the block. Draw vectors with their "tails" on the dot to show the forces exerted *on* the block. Label each force vector and next to it write a brief description of the force.

Copy your group's sketch here after discussion.

In Newtonian physics, all forces are considered as arising from an interaction between *two* objects. Forces are specified by identifying the object *on which* the force is exerted and the object *that is exerting* the force. For example, in the situation above, a gravitational force is exerted *on* the block *by* the Earth.

B. Describe the remaining forces you have indicated above in a similar fashion.

The diagram you have drawn is called a *free-body diagram.* A free-body diagram should show only the forces exerted *on* the object or system of interest (in this case, forces exerted *on the block*). Check your free-body diagram and, if necessary, modify it accordingly.

A proper free-body diagram should *not* have anything on it except a representation of the object and the (labeled) forces exerted on that object. A free-body diagram *never* includes (1) forces exerted by the object of interest on other objects or (2) sketches of other objects that exert forces on the object of interest.

Tutorials in Introductory Physics
McDermott, Shaffer, and the P.E.G., U. Wash.

©Pearson
Custom 2nd Ed., for U.CO, Boulder

C. All forces arise from interactions between objects, but the interactions can take different forms.

Which of the forces exerted on the block require *direct contact* between the block and the object exerting the force?

Which of the forces exerted on the block *do not* arise from direct contact between the block and the object exerting the force?

We will call forces that depend on contact between two objects *contact forces*. We will call forces that do not arise from contact between two objects *non-contact forces*.

D. There are many different types of forces, including: friction ($\vec{f}$), tension ($\vec{T}$), magnetic forces ($\vec{F}^{\text{mag}}$), normal forces ($\vec{N}$), and the gravitational force ($\vec{W}$, for weight). Categorize these forces according to whether they are contact or non-contact forces.

Contact forces   Non-contact forces

E. Consider the following discussion between two students.

Student 1: "I think the free-body diagram for the block should have a force by Chris, a force by the rope, and a force by Pam."

Student 2: "I don't think the diagram should show a force by Pam. People can't exert forces on blocks without touching them."

With which student, if either, do you agree? Explain your reasoning.

It is often useful to label forces in a way that makes clear (1) the type of force, (2) the object on which the force is exerted, and (3) the object exerting the force. For example, the gravitational force exerted *on* the block *by* the Earth might be labeled $\vec{W}_{\text{BE}}$. Your instructor will indicate the notation that you are to use.

F. Label each of the forces on your free-body diagram in part A in the manner described above.

⇨ Do not proceed until a tutorial instructor has checked your free-body diagram.

II. Drawing free-body diagrams

A. Sketch a free-body diagram for a book at rest on a level table.   Book
(*Remember:* A proper free-body diagram should not have anything
on it except a representation of the book and the forces exerted *on* the
book.)

Make sure the label for each force indicates:

• the type of force (gravitational, frictional, *etc.*),

• the object on which the force is exerted, and

• the object exerting the force.

1. What evidence do you have for the existence of each of the forces on your diagram?

2. What observation can you make that allows you to determine the relative magnitudes of
    the forces acting on the book?

How did you show the relative magnitudes of the forces on your diagram?

B. A second book of greater mass is placed on top of the first.   Upper book
                                                                               Lower book
Sketch a free-body diagram for each of the books in the space
below. Label all the forces as in part A.

Free-body diagram for upper book	Free-body diagram for lower book

Specify which of the forces are contact forces and which are non-contact.

1. Examine all the forces on the two free-body diagrams you just drew. Explain why a force that appears on one diagram *should not* appear on the other diagram.

2. What *type* of force does the upper book exert on the lower book (*e.g.*, frictional, gravitational)?

    Why would it be *incorrect* to say that the weight of the upper book acts on the lower book?

3. What observation can you make that allows you to determine the relative magnitudes of the forces on the *upper* book?

4. Are there any forces acting on the *lower* book that have the same magnitude as a force acting on the *upper* book? Explain.

C. Compare the free-body diagram for the lower book to the free-body diagram for the same book in part A (*i.e.*, before the upper book was added).

    Which of the forces changed when the upper book was added and which remained the same?

    As discussed earlier, we think of each force acting on an object as being exerted by another object. The first object exerts a force of equal magnitude and opposite direction on the second object. The two forces together are called an *action-reaction* or *Newton's third law* force pair.

D. Consider the free-body diagrams for both the upper book and the lower book in the context of Newton's third law force pairs.

    1. List below the Newton's third law force pairs for which both members of the pair appear on your free-body diagrams. On which object does each of the forces in the pair act?

       Identify any complete third law force pairs on your diagrams by placing one or more small "×" symbols through each member of the pair. For example, if you have two sets of third law force pairs shown on your diagrams, mark *each* member of the first pair as ⟶×⟶, and *each* member of the second pair as ⟶××⟶.

    2. For each complete third law force pair that you identified in part 1, state whether both members of the pair appear in the *same* free-body diagram, or whether they appear in *different* free-body diagrams.

       Are both members of each third law force pair the *same* type of forces or are they *different* types of forces?

    3. Are any of the forces in your free-body diagrams members of third law force pairs for which the other member does not appear in your diagrams?

       For each such "incomplete" third law force pair that you identify, list:

       • the force that appears in your diagrams,

       • the force that does *not* appear in your diagrams, and

       • the object for which you would need to draw a free-body diagram in order to show the missing force.

    4. Are there any two forces on your diagrams that are equal in magnitude and opposite in direction but that are not members of the same Newton's third law force pair? Explain how you can tell that they do not constitute a third law force pair.

III. Supplement: Contact and non-contact forces

A. A magnet is held up by another magnet as shown at right.

String

Magnet 1

Magnet 2

1. Draw a free-body diagram for magnet 2. The label for each of the forces on your diagram should indicate:

   • the type of force (*e.g.,* gravitational, normal),

   • the object on which the force is exerted, and

   • the object exerting the force.

2. Suppose that the magnets were replaced by stronger magnets of the same mass.

   If this changes the free-body diagram for magnet 2, sketch the new free-body diagram and describe how the diagram changes. (Label the forces as you did in part 1 above.) If the free-body diagram for magnet 2 does not change, explain why it does not.

3. Can a magnet exert a non-contact force on another object?

   Can a magnet exert a contact force on another object?

   Describe how you can use a magnet to exert *both* a contact force and a non-contact force on another magnet.

4. To ensure that you have accounted for all the forces acting on magnet 2 in parts 1 and 2:

   List all the non-contact forces acting on magnet 2.

   List all the contact forces acting on magnet 2. (*Hint:* Which objects are in *contact* with magnet 2?)

Tutorials in Introductory Physics
McDermott, Shaffer, and the P.E.G., U. Wash.

©Pearson
Custom 2nd Ed., for U.CO, Boulder

B. An iron rod is held up by a magnet as shown. The magnet is supported by a string.

String

Magnet

Iron rod

1. In the spaces below, sketch a free-body diagram for the iron rod and a separate free-body diagram for the magnet.

The label for each of the forces on your diagrams should indicate:

- the type of force (*e.g.,* gravitational, normal),
- the object on which the force is exerted, and
- the object exerting the force.

Free-body diagram for iron rod	Free-body diagram for magnet
(*Hint:* There should be three forces.)	(*Hint:* There should be four forces.)

2. For each of the forces shown in your diagram for the iron rod, identify the corresponding force that completes the Newton's third law (or action-reaction) force pair.

3. How would your diagram for the iron rod change if the magnet were replaced with a stronger magnet? Which forces would change (in type or in magnitude)? Which forces would remain the same?

I. Applying Newton's laws to interacting objects: constant speed

Three identical bricks are pushed across a table at *constant speed* as shown. The hand pushes horizontally. (*Note:* There is friction between the bricks and the table.)

Call the stack of two bricks system A and the single brick system B.

A. Compare the *net force* (magnitude and direction) on system A to that on system B. Explain how you arrived at your comparison.

B. Draw separate free-body diagrams for system A and system B. Label each of the forces in your diagrams by identifying: the type of force, the object on which the force is exerted, and the object exerting the force.

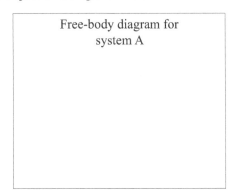

Free-body diagram for
system A

Free-body diagram for
system B

C. Is the magnitude of the force exerted on system A by system B *greater than, less than,* or *equal to* the magnitude of the force exerted on system B by system A? Explain.

   Would your answer change if the hand were pushing system B to the left instead of pushing system A to the right? If so, how? If not, why not?

D. Identify all the Newton's third law (action-reaction) force pairs in your diagrams by placing one or more small "×" symbols through each member of the pair (*i.e.,* mark each member of the first pair as →✶→, each member of the second pair as →✶✶→, *etc.*).

   What criteria did you use to identify the force pair(s)?

   Is your answer to part C consistent with your identification of Newton's third law (or action-reaction) force pairs? If so, explain how it is consistent. If not, resolve the inconsistency.

E. Rank the *horizontal* forces that you identified on your free-body diagrams in part B by magnitude, from largest to smallest. (*Hint:* Recall that the bricks are pushed so that they move at constant speed.)

Did you apply Newton's second law in comparing the magnitudes of the horizontal forces? If so, how?

Did you apply Newton's third law in comparing the magnitudes of the horizontal forces? If so, how?

What information besides Newton's laws did you need to apply in comparing the magnitudes of the horizontal forces?

F. Suppose the mass of each brick is 2.5 kg, the coefficient of kinetic friction between the bricks and the table is 0.2, and the bricks are moving at a constant speed of 0.50 m/s.

Determine the magnitude of each of the forces that you drew on your free-body diagrams in part B. (Use the approximation $g = 10$ m/s^2.)

Would your answers change if the bricks were moving half as fast? If so, how? If not, why not?

⇨ Discuss your answers to section I with a tutorial instructor before continuing.

II. Applying Newton's laws to interacting objects: varying speed

Suppose the bricks were pushed by the hand with the same force as in section I; however, the coefficient of kinetic friction between the bricks and the table is *less than* that in section I.

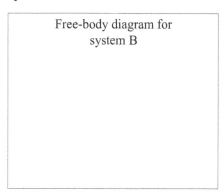

A. Describe the motions of systems A and B. How does the motion compare to that in part I?

B. Compare the *net force* (magnitude and direction) on system A to that on system B. Explain.

C. Draw and label separate free-body diagrams for systems A and B.

Free-body diagram for system A	Free-body diagram for system B

D. Consider the following discussion between two students.

Student 1: "System A and system B are pushed by the same force as before, so they will have the same motion as in section I."

Student 2: "I disagree. I think that they are speeding up since friction is less. So now system A is pushing on system B with a greater force than system B is pushing on system A."

With which student, if either, do you agree? Explain your reasoning.

E. Rank the magnitudes of all the *horizontal* forces that appear on your free-body diagrams in part C. Explain your reasoning. (Describe explicitly how you used Newton's second and third laws to compare the magnitudes of the forces.)

Is it possible to *completely* rank the horizontal forces in this case?

III. Applying Newton's laws to a system of interacting objects

Let C represent the system consisting of all three bricks. The motion of the bricks is the same as in section II.

System C

A. Compare the magnitude of the *net force* on system C to the magnitudes of the *net forces* on systems A and B. Explain.

B. Draw and label a free-body diagram for system C.

Compare the forces that appear on your free-body diagram for system C to those that appear on your diagrams for systems A and B in section II.

For each of the forces that appear on your diagram for system C, list the corresponding force (or forces) on your diagrams for systems A and B.

Free-body diagram for
system C

Are there any forces on your diagrams for systems A and B that you did not list? If so, what characteristic do these forces have in common that none of the others share?

Why is it not necessary to consider these forces in determining the motion of system C?

Note that such forces are sometimes called *internal forces*, to be distinguished from *external forces*.

IV. Interpreting free-body diagrams

At right is a free-body diagram for a cart. All forces have been drawn to scale.

In the space below, sketch the cart, rope, *etc.*, as they would appear in the laboratory.

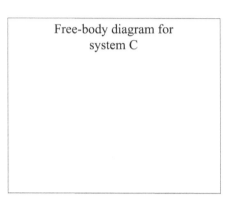

Free-body diagram
for cart

$N_{\text{on cart by table}}$ $T_{\text{on cart by string}}$

$W_{\text{on cart by earth}}$

What can you say about the motion of the cart based on the free-body diagram? For example, could the cart be: moving to the left? moving to the right? stationary? Explain whether each case is possible and, if so, describe the motion of the cart.

Tutorials in Introductory Physics
McDermott, Shaffer, and the P.E.G., U. Wash.

©Pearson
Custom 2nd Ed., for U.CO, Boulder

I. Blocks connected by a rope

Two blocks, A and B, are tied together with a rope of mass *M*. Block B is being pushed with a constant horizontal force as shown at right. Assume that there is no friction between the blocks and the table and that the blocks have already been moving for a while at the instant shown.

Rope has mass M

A. Describe the motions of block A, block B, and the rope.

The blocks are moving to the right.

B. On a large sheet of paper, draw a separate free-body diagram for each block and for the rope. Clearly label the forces.

Copy your free-body diagrams below after discussion.

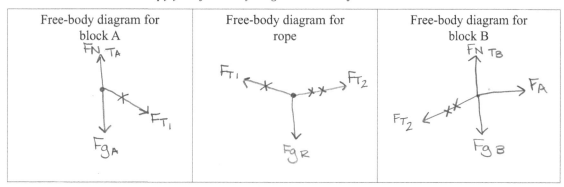

Free-body diagram for block A	Free-body diagram for rope	Free-body diagram for block B

C. Identify all the *Newton's third law (action-reaction)* force pairs in your diagrams by placing one or more small "×" symbols through each member of the pair (*i.e.*, mark each member of the first pair as →×→, each member of the second pair as →××→, *etc.*).

D. Rank, from largest to smallest, the magnitudes of the *horizontal components* of the forces on your diagrams. Explain your reasoning.

E. Consider the horizontal components of the forces exerted *on the rope* by blocks A and B. Is your answer above for the relative magnitudes of these components consistent with your knowledge of the net force on the rope?

⇨ Check your reasoning with a tutorial instructor before proceeding.

Tutorials in Introductory Physics
McDermott, Shaffer, and the P.E.G., U. Wash.

©Pearson
Custom 2nd Ed., for U.CO, Boulder

II. Blocks connected by a very light string

The blocks in section I are now connected with a very light, flexible, and inextensible string of mass m $(m < M)$.

String has mass m

A. If the motion of the blocks is the same as in section I, how does the net force on the *string* compare to the net force on the *rope?*

the net force

1. Determine whether the net force on each of the following is *greater than, less than,* or *equal to* the net force on the corresponding object or system in section I. Explain.

   • block A

   • block B

   • the system composed of the blocks and the connecting string

2. Compare the horizontal components of the following pairs of forces:

   • the force on the string by block A and the force on the rope by block A. Explain.

   • the force on the string by block B and the force on the rope by block B. Explain.

B. Suppose the mass of the string that connects blocks A and B becomes smaller and smaller, but the motion remains the same as in section I. What happens to:

   • the magnitude of the net force on that connecting string?

   • the magnitudes of the forces exerted on that connecting string by blocks A and B?

C. A string exerts a force on each of the two objects to which it is attached. For a massless string, the magnitude of both forces is often referred to as "the tension in the string."

   Justify the use of this approach, in which a *single value* is assumed for the magnitude of both forces.

Tutorials in Introductory Physics
McDermott, Shaffer, and the P.E.G., U. Wash.

©Pearson
Custom 2nd Ed., for U.CO, Boulder

D. If you know that the net force on a massless string is zero, what, if anything, can you infer about its motion?

Is it possible to exert a non-zero force on a massless string? Is it possible for a massless string to have a non-zero *net* force? Explain.

⇨ Discuss your answers above with a tutorial instructor before continuing.

III. The Atwood's machine

The Atwood's machine at right consists of two identical objects connected by a massless string that runs over an ideal pulley. Object B is initially held so that it is above object A and so that neither object can move.

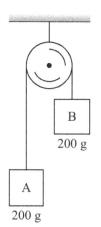

A. Predict the subsequent motions of objects A and B after they are released. Explain the basis for your description. Do not use algebra.

neither object will move when released.

B. Draw separate free-body diagrams for objects A and B. Are your free-body diagrams consistent with your prediction of the motion of the objects?

C. Object C is replaced by object C, of greater mass. Object C is initially held so that it is higher than object A and so that neither object can move.

Predict:

• what will happen to object C when it is released.

• how the motion of object C will compare to the motion of object A after they are released.

Explain the basis for your predictions. Do not use algebra.

D. Draw and label separate free-body diagrams for objects A and C *after* they are released. Indicate the relative magnitudes of the forces by the relative lengths of the force vectors.

Are the predictions you made in part C consistent with your free-body diagrams for objects A and C? If so, explain why they are consistent. If not, then resolve the inconsistency.

E. The weight of a 200 g mass has magnitude $(0.2 \text{ kg})(9.8 \text{ m/s}^2) \approx 2$ N. Similarly, the weight of a 400 g mass is approximately 4 N in magnitude.

   1. How does the force exerted on object A by the string compare to these two weights?

   2. How does the force exerted on object C by the string compare to these two weights?

      Explain your answers.

   3. How does the net force on object A compare to the net force on object C? Explain.

F. Consider the following statement about the Atwood's machine made by a student.

   "All strings can do is transmit forces from other objects. That means that the string in the Atwood's machine just transmits the weight of one block to the other: the force upward on each block is equal to the weight of the other block."

   Do you agree with this student? Explain your reasoning.

Tutorials in Introductory Physics
McDermott, Shaffer, and the P.E.G., U. Wash.

©Pearson
Custom 2nd Ed., for U.CO, Boulder

I. Relating work, force, and displacement

A. The figure at right shows a hand pushing a block as it moves through a displacement $\Delta\vec{s}$.

Direction of original force

$\Delta\vec{s}$

1. Suppose instead the force exerted by the hand were directed partially downward as shown. Both the displacement of the block and the magnitude of the force are the same as before.

   Would the work done by the new force be *greater than*, *less than*, or *equal to* the work done by the original force? Explain.

   The work done would be less than the original force because only the horizontal component is causing the block to move.

   Direction of new force

   $\Delta\vec{s}$

2. Suppose instead that the hand were to push with a force of the same magnitude as before but do zero work. The displacement of the block is the same as before. In the space at right, draw an arrow to show the direction of the force by the hand.

Displacement of block	Force on block by hand
←	↓ or ↑

B. A block is initially moving to the right on a level, frictionless surface. A hand exerts a constant horizontal force on the block that causes the block to slow down (stage 1), turn around, then move in the opposite direction while speeding up (stage 2).

1. Complete the table below. Draw arrows to indicate relevant directions, and take the positive *x*-direction to the right.

	Displacement		Force by hand		Work done
	Direction	Sign	Direction	Sign	Sign
Stage 1	→	+	←	−	−
Stage 2	←	−	←	−	+

2. Which entries in the table, if any, would differ if instead the positive *x*-direction were to the left? Explain your reasoning.

   sign of displacement in both directions
   force by hand for both stages

   the sign of the work does not depend on the coor. systems

3. Consider the following statement:

   "The force is always to the left. So if left is negative, then the work done is negative in both stages. If we change the coordinate system and make left positive, then the work is positive in both cases." Direction of

   Do you agree or disagree with this statement? Explain.

C. Summarize your results thus far by explaining how to determine the sign and absolute value of the work done on an object subject to a single force.

We now consider work done on systems in which different parts of the system undergo different displacements.

Tutorials in Introductory Physics
McDermott, Shaffer, and the P.E.G., U. Wash.

©Pearson
Custom 2nd Ed., for U.CO, Boulder

II. Work done on systems

Two identical blocks, A and B, are initially at rest on a level, frictionless surface. At time $t = t_1$, hands begin to push the blocks toward each other as shown at right. Each hand exerts a constant horizontal force of magnitude F_o. At time $t = t_2$, each block has moved a distance d_o from its initial position.

A. During the interval from t_1 to t_2:

   1. Is the work done on block A by the hand *positive, negative,* or *zero?* Explain.

   2. Is the work done on block B by the hand *positive, negative,* or *zero?* Explain.

   The sum of the works done by all external forces exerted on an object or system is called the *net work by external forces, $W_{net\ ext}$.*

B. Consider system T, consisting of blocks A and B. Write an expression for the net work done on system T by external forces during the interval from t_1 to t_2 in terms of the given quantities. Explain.

C. Write an expression for the *net force* on system T at an instant between t_1 and t_2. Could you use this net force to calculate the net work on system T by external forces? Explain.

D. Consider the following statement:

   "Since both blocks move the same distance, but in opposite directions, the system hasn't really moved. Therefore, the net work on the system is zero."

   Do you agree or disagree with this statement? Explain.

   In your own words, explain what displacement(s) should be used to calculate the net work on a system in which different parts of the system undergo different displacements.

   ⇨ Discuss your answers with a tutorial instructor before continuing.

Tutorials in Introductory Physics
McDermott, Shaffer, and the P.E.G., U. Wash.

©Pearson
Custom 2nd Ed., for U.CO, Boulder

III. Relating work and changes in kinetic energy for particle-like systems

A. Use the definition of kinetic energy to determine the sign of the *change in kinetic energy, ΔK,* for an object that is (1) speeding up, (2) slowing down, or (3) moving at constant speed.

B. Use your results thus far to complete the table at right.

	Part I.B Stage 1	Part I.B Stage 2	Part II Block A	Part II Block B
Sign of ΔK				
Sign of $W_{\text{net ext}}$				

The net work done on a system by external forces causes a change in the total energy of that system. In parts I and II, the only form of energy being changed is the kinetic energy, so $W_{\text{net ext}} = \Delta K$.

C. Check that your results in the table above are consistent with the expression $W_{\text{net ext}} = \Delta K$.

IV. Applying $W_{\text{net ext}} = \Delta K$

Two carts, C and D, are initially at rest on a horizontal frictionless table as shown in the top-view diagram below. A constant force of magnitude F_o is exerted on each cart as it travels between two marks on the table. Cart D has a greater mass than cart C.

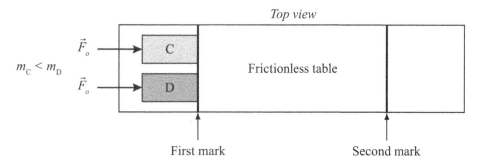

A. Do you agree or disagree with the statement below regarding the final kinetic energy of each cart? Explain.

"Since the same force is exerted on both carts, the cart with the smaller mass will move quickly, while the cart with the larger mass will move slowly. Since the velocity is squared to get the kinetic energy but mass isn't, the cart with the bigger speed must have more kinetic energy."

B. Is the net work done on cart C by external forces ($W_{net\ ext,\ C}$) *greater than, less than,* or *equal to* the net work done on cart D by external forces ($W_{net\ ext,\ D}$)? Explain.

After both carts have passed the second mark, is the kinetic energy of cart C *greater than, less than,* or *equal to* the kinetic energy of cart D?

C. Are your answers to parts A and B consistent with one another? Explain. If you no longer agree with the statement in part A, describe why you think it is incorrect.

V. Limitations of $W_{net\ ext} = \Delta K$

Suppose that the experiment described in part II were repeated with a spring between blocks A and B as shown at right. This time, the blocks start from rest at time t_3 and come to rest at time t_4 after having moved a distance d_o from their initial positions.

A. Let system Y consist of blocks A and B and the spring.

Determine the *net work by external forces* on system Y during the interval from t_3 to t_4. (*Hint:* How do the external forces on the system in parts II and V compare?) Explain.

B. Explain how your answer is *inconsistent* with $W_{net\ ext} = \Delta K$.

The relationship $W_{net\ ext} = \Delta K$ is appropriate for systems that undergo no changes in internal energy. When the spring above changes length, the energy stored in it changes. As we will see in the tutorial *Conservation of energy,* the work-energy theorem can be extended to a more general form.

Tutorials in Introductory Physics
McDermott, Shaffer, and the P.E.G., U. Wash.

©Pearson
Custom 2nd Ed., for U.CO, Boulder

I. Relating work and changes in energy

Two experiments are conducted with identical blocks on a level, frictionless surface. Each block starts from rest and is pushed through a distance d_o by a hand that exerts a constant horizontal force of magnitude F_o.

In experiment 1, the blocks are connected by an ideal massless spring of constant k_1, which is initially neither stretched nor compressed. At the end of the interval shown, each block has a speed of zero.

In experiment 2, each block has a speed of v_{f2} at the end of the interval shown.

A. Consider system 1 (which consists of the two blocks and the spring in experiment 1) and system 2 (which consists of the two blocks in experiment 2).

In the table below, indicate whether each of the quantities is *positive*, *negative*, or *zero* for systems 1 and 2. Explain. (*Note:* ΔU represents the change in potential energy of the system.)

	$W_{\text{net ext}}$	ΔK	ΔU	ΔE_{tot}
System 1	$+$	0	$+$	$+$
System 2	$+$	$+$	0	$+$

B. State whether each of the statements below is consistent with your results above. If not, cite a specific case from the table that contradicts the student's statement.

Student 1: "The net work done on a system is always equal to the change in kinetic energy of that system."

Student 2: "In the absence of friction, the total energy of a system must remain constant. In other words, $K_i + U_i = K_f + U_f$."

Student 3: "The total energy of a system can change if something is doing work on that system. The net work done on a system by external forces is equal to the change in total energy of the system."

⇨ Discuss your answers with a tutorial instructor before continuing.

A fundamental principle of physics is that the total energy of a system changes only through interactions with objects outside that system. One way to change the total energy of a system is through work done by external forces. The net work done on a system by external forces and the change in energy of that system are related by the principle of conservation of energy. In mechanics, this principle can be expressed as:

$$W_{\text{net ext}} = \Delta E_{\text{tot}}$$

C. Experiment 1 is repeated using an ideal massless spring of constant k_3, which is less than k_1. As in experiment 1, the spring is initially neither stretched nor compressed, and each block starts from rest and is pushed through a distance d_o by a hand that exerts a constant horizontal force of magnitude F_o. However, at the end of experiment 3, each block has a speed of v_{f3}.

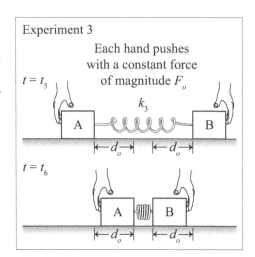

Experiment 3

Each hand pushes with a constant force of magnitude F_o

System 3 consists of the two blocks and the spring in experiment 3.

1. Rank the three systems according to *the absolute value of the net work by external forces,* from largest to smallest. If the net work on any of the systems is zero, state so explicitly. Explain.

   all 3 systems have equal network

2. Rank the three systems according to *the absolute value of the change in total energy,* from largest to smallest. If the change in energy of any of the systems is zero, state so explicitly. Explain.

3. Rank the three systems according to *the absolute value of the change in potential energy,* from largest to smallest. If the change in potential energy of any of the systems is zero, state so explicitly. Explain.

4. Rank the three systems according to *the absolute value of the change in kinetic energy,* from largest to smallest. If the change in kinetic energy of any of the systems is zero, state so explicitly. Explain.

Tutorials in Introductory Physics
McDermott, Shaffer, and the P.E.G., U. Wash.

©Pearson
Custom 2nd Ed., for U.CO, Boulder

5. Is it possible to rank the changes in total energy of the three systems by simply comparing the rankings of change in potential and kinetic energy for the systems (*i.e.*, without comparing the net work on the systems)? Explain.

Experiment 2 has the highest $\Delta k \rightarrow$ Exp. 1 $\rightarrow$ exp 3

no.

D. In order for the equation $K_i + U_i = K_f + U_f$ to be true for a given system, what must be true about the net work on that system? Explain. (*Hint:* Rearrange the terms to express the equation in terms of ΔK and ΔU. How are these related to the change in total energy of the system?)

$K_i + K_f + K_f + U_f = 0$

II. Systems

A block of mass m on a frictionless surface is attached to an ideal massless spring of constant k, as shown at right. When the block is at $x = 0$, the spring is neither stretched nor compressed. At time t_i, the block is released from rest at $x = x_i$. At time t_f, the block passes $x = 0$ moving to the left with speed v_f.

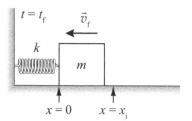

A. Consider system A, which consists of *the block and the spring*.

1. List all the forces acting on system A during the interval from t_i to t_f. For each force, indicate the object exerting the force and the type of force.

2. For each force that you listed above, state whether that force does *positive, negative,* or *zero* work on system A during the interval from t_i to t_f. Explain.

3. Write an expression for each of the following quantities for the interval from t_i to t_f. Express your answer in terms of given variables. If any of the quantities are zero, state so explicitly. Explain.

ΔK_A	ΔU_A	$W_{\text{net ext, A}}$

4. Write an equation that relates these expressions. Explain.

5. Solve this equation for v_f, the final speed of the block, in terms of given variables.

B. Now consider system B, which consists of *the block only*.

1. List all the forces acting on system B during the interval from t_i to t_f. For each force, indicate the object exerting the force and the type of force.

2. For each force that you listed above, state whether that force does *positive, negative,* or *zero* work on system B during the interval from t_i to t_f. Explain.

3. Write an expression for each of the following quantities for the interval from t_i to t_f. If any of the quantities are zero, state so explicitly. Explain.

ΔK_B	ΔU_B	$W_{net\ ext,\ B}$

4. Write an equation that relates these expressions. Explain.

5. Consider the following student discussion about system B:

   Student 1: "The spring does work on the block, which changes the potential energy of the block. So we need to write $W_{net\ ext,\ B} = \Delta K + \Delta U$."

   Student 2: "But $W_{net\ ext,\ B}$ and ΔU are both equal to $\frac{1}{2} k x_i^2$, so they will cancel out in that equation, and we won't be able to solve for the final velocity of the block."

   Student 3: "I think the system can only have a change in spring potential energy if the spring is inside the system. Since the spring is outside the system in this case, the change in potential energy of the system is zero."

   With which student(s), if any, do you agree? Explain.

6. Check that your responses to questions 4 and 5 are consistent with one another. If they are not, explain how you would change your answers to make them consistent.

7. Solve your equation from question 4 for v_f, the final speed of the block, in terms of given variables. Check that your answer is consistent with your answer to part A.5.

C. Answer the following questions on the basis of your results from parts A and B:

  1. Does the spring contribute to, or have any effect on, the energy of system A (*i.e.,* when the spring *is* part of the system)? If so, explain how. If not, explain why not.

  2. Does the spring contribute to, or have any effect on, the energy of system B (*i.e.,* when the spring is *not* part of the system)? If so, explain how. If not, explain why not.

⇨ Discuss your answers with a tutorial instructor.

I. Relating forces to changes in kinetic energy and momentum

Two carts, A and B, are initially at rest on a horizontal frictionless table as shown in the top-view diagram below. A constant force of magnitude F_o is exerted on each cart as it travels between two marks on the table. Cart B has a greater mass than cart A.

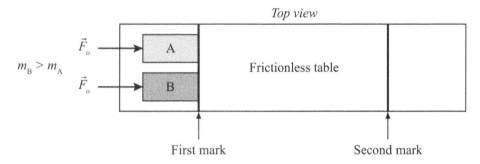

Top view

$m_B > m_A$

A. Three students discuss the final momentum and kinetic energy of each cart.

     Student 1:   "Since the same force is exerted on both carts, the cart with the smaller mass will move quickly, while the cart with the larger mass will move slowly. The momentum of each cart is equal to its mass times its velocity."

     Student 2:   "This must mean that the speed compensates for the mass and the two carts have equal final momenta."

     Student 3:   "I was thinking about the kinetic energies. Since the velocity is squared to get the kinetic energy but mass isn't, the cart with the bigger speed must have more kinetic energy."

In the space below, write down whether you agree or disagree with the statements made by each student.

B. Which cart takes longer to travel between the two marks? Explain your reasoning.

C. Use Newton's second law and the definition of acceleration to derive an equation for each cart relating the net force on the cart to the change in velocity of the cart ($\Delta \vec{v}_A$ or $\Delta \vec{v}_B$) and the time interval (Δt_A or Δt_B) that the cart spends between the two marks.

     1. Is the quantity $m_A|\Delta \vec{v}_A|$ *greater than*, *less than*, or *equal to* $m_B|\Delta \vec{v}_B|$? Explain how you can tell.

For a constant net force, the quantity $\vec{F}_{net}\,\Delta t$ is called the *impulse* imparted to the object.

2. Is the magnitude of the impulse imparted to cart A *greater than, less than,* or *equal to* the magnitude of the impulse imparted to cart B? Explain your reasoning.

3. Write an equation showing how the impulse imparted to cart A is related to the *change in momentum vector* of cart A ($\Delta \vec{p}_A$), where momentum, denoted by $\vec{p}$, is the product of the mass and velocity of the object.

This relationship is known as the *impulse-momentum theorem.*

4. Is the magnitude of the final momentum of cart A (p_{Af}) *greater than, less than,* or *equal to* the magnitude of the final momentum of cart B (p_{Bf})? Explain.

D. How does the net work done on cart A ($W_{net\,A}$) compare to the net work done on cart B ($W_{net\,B}$)? Explain.

Is the kinetic energy of cart A *greater than, less than,* or *equal to* the kinetic energy of cart B after they have passed the second mark?

E. Refer again to the discussion among the three students in part A. Do you agree with your original answer?

If you disagree with any of the students, identify what is incorrect with their statements.

⇨ Discuss your answers to parts C and D with a tutorial instructor before continuing.

II. Applying the work-energy and impulse-momentum theorems

Obtain a wedge, a ball, a
cardboard ramp, and
enlargements of the two diagrams
below (or sketch them on a large
sheet of paper).

(*Note:* It is important that each
time the ball is rolled it has the
same speed on the level region I.
Place a mark halfway up the
wedge and release the ball from
the mark each time.) Ignore
friction and the rotation of the
ball.

A. Release the ball so that it rolls
straight toward the ramp (motion 1).

Observe the motion of the ball.

Sketch the trajectory of the ball on
an enlargement for motion 1.

On the enlargement, draw arrows to
show the directions of (1) the
acceleration of the ball and (2) the
net force on the ball while it is on the
ramp (*i.e.*, in region II).

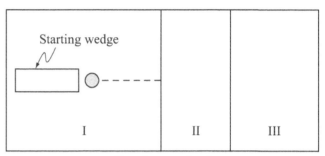

Top view, motion 1

B. Release the ball at an angle to the
ramp as shown (motion 2).

Observe the motion of the ball.

Sketch the trajectory of the ball on
an enlargement for motion 2.

On the enlargement, draw arrows to
show the directions of (1) the
acceleration of the ball and (2) the
net force on the ball while it is on the
ramp (*i.e.*, in region II).

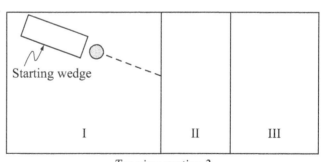

Top view, motion 2

C. How does the direction of the net force on the ball in motion 2 compare to the direction of the net force on the ball in motion 1? Explain.

   Is the direction of the acceleration of the ball in motion 2 consistent with the fact that the ball speeds up and its trajectory curves? Explain.

D. How does the change in kinetic energy of the ball in motion 1 compare to the change in kinetic energy of the ball in motion 2?

   1. Is your answer consistent with the net work done on the ball in motions 1 and 2? Explain.

   2. How does the final speed of the ball in motion 1 compare to the final speed in motion 2? Explain.

E. For motion 1, draw vectors in region II of the enlargement that represent the momentum of the ball at the top of the ramp and at the bottom of the ramp (*i.e.*, at the top and bottom of region II). Use these vectors to construct the change in momentum vector $\Delta\vec{p}$.

   How is the direction of $\Delta\vec{p}$ related to the direction of the net force on the ball as it rolls down the ramp? Is your answer consistent with the impulse-momentum theorem?

F. For motion 2, draw vectors in region II of the enlargement that represent the initial and the final momentum of the ball. Draw these vectors using the same scale that you used for motion 1 (*i.e.*, the relative lengths should represent the relative magnitudes). Use these vectors to construct the change in momentum vector $\Delta\vec{p}$ for motion 2.

How should the direction of $\Delta\vec{p}$ compare to the direction of the net force on the ball as it rolls down the ramp? If necessary, modify your diagram to be consistent with the impulse-momentum theorem.

G. Consider the change in momentum vectors you constructed for motions 1 and 2.

1. How do they compare in direction? How do they compare in magnitude?

2. On the basis of your answer above, compare the time that the ball spends on the ramp in motion 1 to the time it spends on the ramp in motion 2. Explain. (*Hint:* Can you use the impulse-momentum theorem to compare the time intervals?)

Is your answer consistent with the trajectory of the ball in each motion? Explain.

I. Momentum as a vector

The momentum, $\vec{p}$, of an object is defined as the product of its mass and its velocity: $\vec{p} = m\vec{v}$.

The momentum of a system of multiple objects is defined as the sum of the momenta of the

individual objects: $\vec{p}_{system} = \vec{p}_1 + \vec{p}_2 + \vec{p}_3 + \dots$.

A. Two small boats, A and B, are in a lake. An observer on the shore sees the boats moving with the same velocity, 1 m/s due east. The mass of boat A is 10 kg, and the mass of boat B is 5 kg.

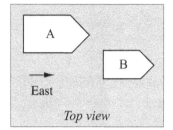

1. Determine the magnitude and direction of the momentum of each boat.

2. Consider system C, the system of the boats A and B together. Determine the magnitude and direction of the momentum of system C. Explain.

B. Later, an observer on the shore sees the boats moving with different velocities. Boat A moves with velocity 3 m/s due west, and boat B moves with velocity 5 m/s due east.

1. Determine the magnitude and direction of the momentum of each boat.

2. Determine the magnitude and direction of the momentum of system C. Explain.

Tutorials in Introductory Physics
McDermott, Shaffer, and the P.E.G., U. Wash.

©Pearson
Custom 2nd Ed., for U.CO, Boulder

II. Momentum of objects in a collision

A. Experiment 1 is conducted with two gliders, A_1 and B_1, on a level, frictionless track. The mass of glider B_1 is greater than that of glider A_1 (*i.e.*, $m_{B_1} > m_{A_1}$).

In experiment 1, glider A_1 moves toward glider B_1, which is initially at rest. Magnets are attached to the gliders so that the gliders repel each other without touching. After the collision, glider A_1 has reversed direction as shown below.

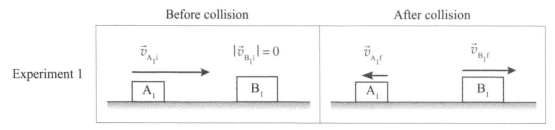

1. In the spaces below, draw vectors to represent the momentum of glider A_1, glider B_1, and system S_1 (the system of both gliders) both before and after the collision. Your vectors need only be qualitatively correct (*e.g.*, any vectors that have the same magnitude should be the same length, and a vector that has a greater magnitude should be longer).

2. Is the magnitude of the final momentum of glider B_1, $|\vec{p}_{Bf}|$, *greater than*, *less than*, or *equal to* the magnitude of the final momentum of system S_1, $|\vec{p}_{S_1f}|$? Explain.

How, if at all, would your answer differ if glider A_1 had instead moved to the right after the collision? Explain.

3. Consider the following statement made by a student about experiment 1:

"Glider A_1 is still moving after the collision. Glider A_1 keeps some of the momentum that it had initially, giving B_1 only a portion of it. There is a limited amount of momentum in the system, and the most any one object can have is all of the system's momentum. Therefore, p_{B1f} must be less than p_{S1f}."

Do you agree or disagree with the statement? Explain.

4. Check that your answer to question 2 is consistent with your answer to question 3 and with the law of conservation of momentum.

Tutorials in Introductory Physics
McDermott, Shaffer, and the P.E.G., U. Wash.

©Pearson
Custom 2nd Ed., for U.CO, Boulder

B. Two additional experiments are performed that are identical to the first with one exception: the mass of the target glider is larger in each subsequent experiment (*i.e.*, $m_{B_3} > m_{B_2} > m_{B_1}$). (The incoming gliders A_1, A_2, and A_3 are identical and have the same initial velocity.)

The final velocities of all gliders are specified in the diagram at right.

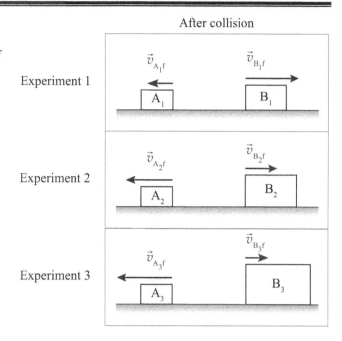

1. Rank the target gliders (B_1, B_2, and B_3) according to *magnitude of final momentum,* from largest to smallest. Explain your reasoning.

2. Complete the momentum vector diagrams below for experiments 1, 2, and 3 (*i.e.*, draw vectors to represent the momentum of the incoming glider, the target glider, and the system before and after the collision). Compare your diagrams with your partners, and resolve any inconsistencies.

3. Check that your momentum vector diagrams are consistent with your ranking in question 1. If not, resolve the inconsistency.

C. Experiments 4–100 are set up in the same pattern as the first three experiments. The mass of glider B_{100} is *much larger* than the mass of glider A_{100}.

In experiment 100, it is observed that:

- the final speed of glider B_{100} is very nearly zero, and

- glider A_{100} moves to the left with a final speed very nearly equal to its initial speed.

1. Is the magnitude of the final momentum of glider B_{100} *greater than, less than,* or *equal to* the magnitude of the initial momentum of glider A_{100}? Explain.

2. Consider the following student dialogue about the final momentum of glider B_{100}:

Student 1: "The final speed of A_{100} is almost the same as its initial speed. This means that A kept almost all of the momentum, giving B almost no momentum."

Student 2: "Right. You can also see that the momentum of B_{100} has to be nearly zero because momentum is mass times velocity. If B's velocity is very small, then its momentum must also be very small."

Student 3: "From each experiment to the next, the mass of B goes up, while its final speed goes down. Therefore, the final momentum of B most likely stays the same."

Describe the error(s) in reasoning in any incorrect statements.

D. Suppose that glider A_{100} has initial momentum 3 kg-m/s to the right, and after the collision, glider A_{100} has final momentum very nearly equal to 3 kg-m/s to the left. What is the magnitude and direction of the final momentum of glider B_{100}? Show your work.

III. Changes in momentum of a system of multiple objects

A. An experiment is performed on a level, frictionless track using two gliders, C and D, of equal mass. Glider D is fixed in place. Glider C is launched toward glider D and rebounds with the same speed that it had initially.

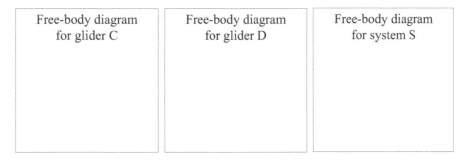

1. In the spaces provided, draw separate free-body diagrams for each glider and for the system of the two gliders at an instant during the collision.

Free-body diagram for glider C	Free-body diagram for glider D	Free-body diagram for system S

   Explain how the fact that glider D is fixed in place is reflected in your free-body diagrams.

2. Does the momentum of each of the following change during the collision? Explain.

   - glider C

   - glider D

   - system S

B. Consider the collisions described in parts II and III. When the momentum of an object or system of objects did not change:

   - were *external* forces exerted on the object or system?

   - was there a *net* force on the object or system?

C. On the basis of your results above, describe how you can tell whether the momentum of an object or system is constant by inspecting the free-body diagram for that object or system.

D. Consider the following student discussion about the above experiment.

Student 1: "This experiment is just like experiment 100. The momentum of glider C is the same before and after the collision—only the direction of motion is different."

Student 2: "Right. Glider D has no momentum afterwards, just like glider B_{100}. So the momentum of the system is unchanged."

Describe the *error* in each statement.

I. Changes in momentum for interacting objects

Two blocks connected by a massless spring are on top of a frictionless, level table. The blocks are pulled apart slightly so that the spring is stretched, and while they are held apart they are given identical initial velocities in a direction perpendicular to the spring. The blocks are then released at the same time.

The mass of block A is two and a half times the mass of block B.

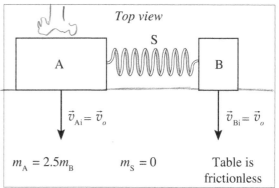

Top view

$\vec{v}_{Ai} = \vec{v}_o$ $\vec{v}_{Bi} = \vec{v}_o$

$m_A = 2.5m_B$ $m_S = 0$ Table is frictionless

A. Draw separate free-body diagrams for each block and for the spring immediately after release. Indicate separately the *vertical* forces (perpendicular to the table top) and the *horizontal* forces (parallel to the table top). Clearly label all forces.

Free-body diagram for block A	Free-body diagram for spring	Free-body diagram for block B
Vertical forces F_N ↑ F_g ↓	Vertical forces N/A	Vertical forces F_N ↑ F_g ↓
Horizontal forces •——→ F_T	Horizontal forces F_T ←——•——→ F_T	Horizontal forces F_T ←——•

Identify all the *Newton's third law (action-reaction)* force pairs in your diagrams by placing one or more small "×" symbols through each member of the pair (*i.e.*, mark each member of the first pair as ⟶×⟶, each member of the second pair as ⟶××⟶, *etc.*).

B. Rank the magnitudes of all the *horizontal* forces on your diagrams. If any of the horizontal forces have the same magnitude, state that explicitly. Explain how Newton's second and third laws can be used to arrive at this ranking.

all horizontal forces have the same magnitude, N3

How does the net force on block A compare to the net force on block B? Discuss both magnitude and direction.

The net force on A is equal & opposite to the net force on block B

Does this comparison of the net forces hold true for all times following the release of the blocks? Explain your reasoning.

yes

Tutorials in Introductory Physics
McDermott, Shaffer, and the P.E.G., U. Wash.

©Pearson
Custom 2nd Ed., for U.CO, Boulder

C. The velocity vectors for blocks A and B are shown for a time immediately before release. Draw a change in velocity vector for each block for a small time interval Δt after release.

$\vec{v}_{Ai}$	$\vec{v}_{Bi}$	$\Delta\vec{v}_A$	$\Delta\vec{v}_B$

Explain how Newton's second law and the definition of acceleration can be used to determine the directions of the change in velocity vectors.

By what factor is the magnitude of $\Delta\vec{v}_B$ greater than the magnitude of $\Delta\vec{v}_A$? Explain.

The magnitude of of $\Delta\vec{v}_B$ is 2.5 greater

How does $m_B\Delta\vec{v}_B$ compare to $m_A\Delta\vec{v}_A$ for this small time interval?

$m_B\Delta\vec{v}_B = m_A\Delta\vec{v}_A$ *for this time period*

Would this comparison change if we considered:

• another interval of time, equally small, occurring much later?

• a much larger time interval?

Explain. *no, the comparison would not change because momentum for the system would be conserved at any point.*

D. Use your knowledge of the velocities and changes in velocities to construct *momentum vectors* and *change in momentum vectors* for the blocks. Also draw a final momentum vector for each block corresponding to the same small time interval as in part C. Show the correct relative magnitudes.

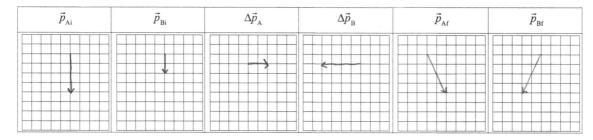

$\vec{p}_{Ai}$	$\vec{p}_{Bi}$	$\Delta\vec{p}_A$	$\Delta\vec{p}_B$	$\vec{p}_{Af}$	$\vec{p}_{Bf}$

Explain how you determined these vectors.

How would $\Delta\vec{p}_A$ compare to $\Delta\vec{p}_B$ if we considered a much larger time interval? Explain.

Overall the system would always have the same momentum but as $\Delta\vec{p}_A$ gets smaller, $\Delta\vec{p}_B$ will get larger.

II. Changes in momentum for systems of interacting objects

Let system C denote the combined system of blocks A and B and the spring S.

A. Draw and label a free-body diagram for system C at a time following the release of the blocks. Indicate separately the *vertical* forces (perpendicular to the table top) and the *horizontal* forces (parallel to the table top). Show separately the net force on system C.

Free-body diagram for system C	Net force on system C
Vertical forces $\vec{F}_N$ ↑ • ↓ $\vec{F}_g$	O
Horizontal forces N/A	

Which forces in your free-body diagrams in section I are *internal forces* for system C?

B. Write an equation for the momentum of system C in terms of the momenta of its constituent bodies.

Compare the momentum of system C *immediately* after the blocks are released to its momentum at the following times:

• a short time later, when the blocks have undergone the change in momentum indicated in section I, and

• a much longer time later.

Explain how you determined your answers.

C. Generalize from your results to answer the following question: Under what condition will the momentum of a system be conserved?

D. Imagine a single object whose mass is equal to the mass of system C and whose momentum is equal at all times to $\vec{p}_C$. Draw an arrow that represents the direction of the velocity of that object. If the velocity is zero, state that explicitly.

Direction of $\vec{v}$

The velocity that you have found is called the velocity of the *center of mass*, $\vec{v}_{cm}$, of system C.

III. Application of momentum conservation to collisions in two dimensions

The spring formerly connecting blocks A and B is disconnected from block B. The blocks are given initial velocities in the directions shown so that they will collide with the spring between them. As in section II, system C refers to the combination of both blocks and spring.

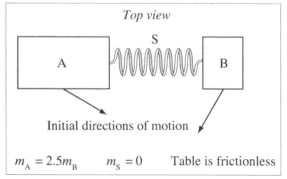

Top view

S

A

B

Initial directions of motion

$m_A = 2.5m_B$ $m_S = 0$ Table is frictionless

A. What are the *external* forces exerted on system C during the collision?

What is the *net force* on system C?

there is no net force

B. The momentum vectors of each block before the collision and of block B after the collision are shown. Complete the table to show the momentum vectors of system C before and after the collision and of block A after the collision.

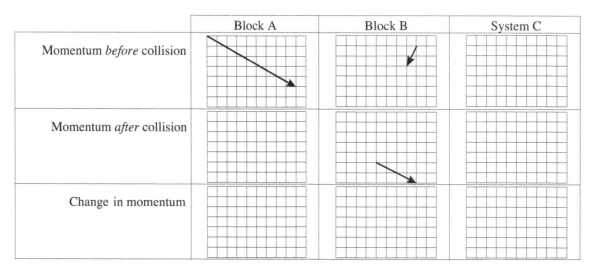

	Block A	Block B	System C
Momentum *before* collision			
Momentum *after* collision			
Change in momentum			

How do the final speeds of the blocks compare? Explain.

C. Draw arrows that represent the direction of the velocity of the center of mass of system C *before* and *after* the collision.

As a result of the collision, does the speed of the center of mass of system C *increase, decrease,* or *stay the same?* Explain.

Direction of $\vec{v}_{cm_i}$	Direction of $\vec{v}_{cm_f}$

Tutorials in Introductory Physics
McDermott, Shaffer, and the P.E.G., U. Wash.

©Pearson
Custom 2nd Ed., for U.CO, Boulder

I. Motion with constant angular velocity

A wheel is spinning *counterclockwise* at a constant rate about a
fixed axis. The diagram at right represents a snapshot of the wheel
at one instant in time.

A. Draw arrows on the diagram to represent the direction of the
velocity for each of the points *A, B,* and *C* at the instant shown.
Explain your reasoning.

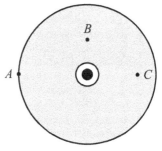

Top view
Wheel spins *counterclockwise*

Is the time taken by points *B* and *C* to move through one
complete circle *greater than, less than,* or *equal to* the time
taken by point *A?*

On the basis of your answer above, determine how the speeds of points *A, B,* and *C*
compare. Explain.

B. Mark the position of each of the labeled points at a later time
when the wheel has completed one half of a turn. Sketch a
velocity vector at each point.

For each labeled point, how does the velocity compare to
the velocity at the earlier time in part A? Discuss both
magnitude and direction.

Top view
Wheel spins *counterclockwise*

Is there one single *linear velocity vector* that applies to every point on the wheel at all
times? Explain.

Tutorials in Introductory Physics
McDermott, Shaffer, and the P.E.G., U. Wash.

©Pearson
Custom 2nd Ed., for U.CO, Boulder

C. Suppose the wheel makes one complete revolution in 2 seconds.

   1. For each of the following points, find the change in angle (Δθ) of the position vector during one second (*i.e.*, find the angle between the initial and final position vectors).

      • point *A*

      • point *B*

      • point *C*

   2. Find the rate of change in the angle for any point on the wheel.

The rate you calculated above is called the *angular speed* of the wheel, or equivalently, the magnitude of the *angular velocity* of the wheel. The angular velocity is defined to be a vector that points along the axis of rotation and is conventionally denoted by the symbol $\vec{\omega}$ (the Greek letter *omega*). To determine the direction of the angular velocity vector, we imagine an observer on the axis of rotation who is looking toward the object. If the observer sees the object rotating counterclockwise, the angular velocity vector is directed toward the observer; if the observer sees it rotating clockwise, the angular velocity vector is directed away from the observer.

D. Would two observers on either side of a rotating object agree on the *direction* of the angular velocity vector? Explain.

Would two observers who use different points on an object to determine the angular velocity agree on the *magnitude* of the angular velocity vector? Explain.

E. The diagrams at right show top and side views of the spinning wheel in part A.

   On each diagram, draw a vector to represent the angular velocity of the wheel. (Use the convention that ⊙ indicates a vector pointing *out of* the page and ⊗ indicates a vector pointing *into* the page.)

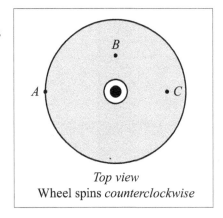

Top view
Wheel spins *counterclockwise*

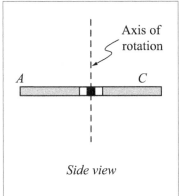

Side view

Tutorials in Introductory Physics
McDermott, Shaffer, and the P.E.G., U. Wash.

©Pearson
Custom 2nd Ed., for U.CO, Boulder

F. In the space at right sketch the position vectors for point C at the beginning and at the end of a small time interval Δ*t*.

Sketch of position vectors at t_o and $t_o + \Delta t$

1. Label the change in angle (Δθ) and the distance between the center of the wheel and point C (*r_C*). Sketch the path taken by point C during this time interval.

What is the distance that point C travels during Δ*t*? Express your answer in terms of r_C and Δθ.

2. Use your answer above and the definition of linear speed to derive an algebraic expression for the linear speed of point C in terms of the angular speed ω of the wheel.

What does your equation imply about the relative linear speeds for points farther and farther out on the wheel? Is this consistent with your answer to part A?

II. Motion with changing angular velocity

A. Let $\vec{\omega}_o$ represent the initial angular velocity of a wheel. In each case described below, determine the magnitude of the *change in angular velocity* $|\Delta\vec{\omega}|$ in terms of $|\vec{\omega}_o|$.

1. The wheel is made to spin faster, so that eventually, a fixed point on the wheel is going around twice as many times each second. (The axis of rotation is fixed.)

2. The wheel is made to spin at the same rate but in the opposite direction.

B. Suppose the wheel slows down uniformly, so that $|\vec{\omega}|$ decreases by 8π rad/s every 4 s. (The wheel continues spinning in the same direction and has the same orientation.)

Specify the angular acceleration $\vec{\alpha}$ of the wheel by giving its magnitude and, relative to $\vec{\omega}$, its direction.

In linear kinematics we find the acceleration vector by first constructing $\Delta\vec{v}$ (a *change in velocity vector*) and then dividing that by Δ*t*. Describe the analogous steps that you used above to find the angular acceleration $\vec{\alpha}$.

⇨ Discuss your answers above with a tutorial instructor before continuing.

III. Torque and angular acceleration

The rigid bar shown at right is free to rotate about a fixed pivot through its center. The axis of rotation of the bar is perpendicular to the plane of the paper.

A. A force of magnitude F_o is applied to point M as shown. The force is *always* at a right angle to the bar.

For each of the following cases, determine whether the angular acceleration would be in a *clockwise* or *counterclockwise* sense.

- The bar was initially at rest. *(Hint: Consider $\Delta \vec{\omega}$.)*

- The bar was spinning at a constant rate before the force was applied.

  Does your answer for the angular acceleration depend on whether the bar was originally spinning clockwise or counterclockwise? Explain.

The application point and direction of a force can affect the rotational motion of the object to which the force is applied. The tendency of a particular force to cause an angular acceleration of an object is quantified as the *torque* produced by the force. The torque $\vec{\tau}$ is defined to be the vector cross product $\vec{r} \times \vec{F}$, where $\vec{r}$ is the vector from the axis of rotation to the point where the force is applied. The magnitude of the torque is simply $|\vec{\tau}| = |\vec{r}| \, |\vec{F}| \, |\sin \theta|$, where θ is the angle between $\vec{r}$ and $\vec{F}$.

B. Compare the magnitude of the *net torque* about the pivot in each case below to that in part A.

1.

2.

3.

4.

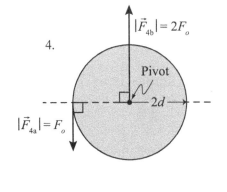

Tutorials in Introductory Physics
McDermott, Shaffer, and the P.E.G., U. Wash.

©Pearson
Custom 2nd Ed., for U.CO, Boulder

I. A spool on a variety of surfaces

Perspective view

A. A spool is pulled across a piece of sandpaper as shown at right. The sandpaper is fixed in place, and the hand pulls horizontally on the thread. The thread has been wrapped around the bottom of the spool many times.

Top view

Spool

1. *Predict* whether the spool will rotate. Explain your reasoning.

2. *Predict* whether the center of the spool will move across the sandpaper. If it will move, describe the direction in which it will move. Explain.

B. Imagine repeating the above experiment on a smooth tabletop *without* the sandpaper.

1. *Predict* whether the spool will rotate. Explain your reasoning.

2. *Predict* whether the center of the spool will move across the table. If it will move, describe the direction in which it will move. Explain.

C. Ask a tutorial instructor to provide you with equipment so that you can check your predictions. Make sure that the thread is wrapped *very close to the bottom of the spool,* so that the spool does not start to tip over when the thread is pulled.

1. When the spool is *on the sandpaper,* and the thread is pulled:

   • Does the spool rotate?

   • Does the center of the spool move? If so, in what general direction does it move?

2. When the spool is *on a smooth tabletop,* and the thread is pulled:

   • Does the spool rotate?

   • Does the center of the spool move? If so, in what general direction does it move?

D. Suppose that you could repeat the experiment using an even smoother surface.

   • Would the spool rotate?

   • Would the center of the spool move? If so, in what direction would it move?

⇨ Discuss your answers with a tutorial instructor before continuing.

II. The block-and-spool problem

A block and a spool are each pulled across a level, frictionless surface by a string, as illustrated at right.

The string pulling the block is tied to a small hook (not shown) at the center of the front face of the block. The string pulling the spool is wrapped many times around the spool and may unwind as it is pulled.

The block and the spool have the same mass. The strings are pulled with the same constant tension and start pulling at the same instant.

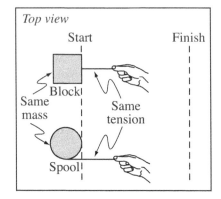

Make the approximation that the strings and the hook are massless.

A. Will the spool cross the finish line *before*, *after*, or *at the same instant as* the block? Explain.

B. Three students discuss the block-and-spool problem:

Student 1: "The spool will rotate, and it will cross the finish line at the same time as the block. They have the same mass and the same net force, so their centers of mass will have the same acceleration. It doesn't matter whether the spool starts rotating—the tension force will still have the same effect on the spool's translational motion."

Student 2: "The spool will rotate, and it will cross after the block. This is because some of the tension force on the spool is being used to rotate the spool. When a force causes an object to rotate, it has less of an effect on the object's translational motion."

Student 3: "The spool will rotate, and it will cross after the block. I was thinking about energy. The spool and block must each have the same total kinetic energy when they get to the finish line. Since the spool will have some rotational kinetic energy, it must have less translational kinetic energy than the block. Therefore, it will be slower, and it will arrive at the finish line later."

With which student(s), if any, do you agree? Explain your reasoning.

In the next section, you will consider a way to test which student's line of reasoning, if any, is correct.

Tutorials in Introductory Physics
McDermott, Shaffer, and the P.E.G., U. Wash.

©Pearson
Custom 2nd Ed., for U.CO, Boulder

III. Testing ideas about combined translation and rotation through an experiment

The apparatus shown at right consists of two identical spools connected by a massless, inextensible thread that runs over an ideal pulley. The thread is wrapped around spool A many times, but it is attached to a fixed point on spool B, so that spool B will not rotate.

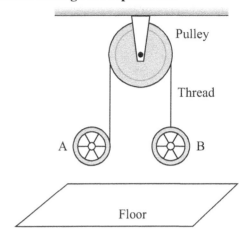

The spools are released from rest from the same height above the floor at the same instant.

A. *Predict* whether spool A will hit the floor *before*, *after*, or *at the same instant as* spool B. If either spool starts to move only after the other spool hits the floor, state that explicitly. Explain.

B. In the space at right, draw an *extended free-body diagram* for each spool immediately after it is released. In an *extended free-body diagram,* draw each vector with its "tail" at the point at which the force is exerted.

C. In the space at right, draw a *(point) free-body diagram* for each spool at the same instant as above. In a *(point) free-body diagram,* draw each vector with its "tail" on the dot, as usual.

D. Recall the student dialogue in the previous section.

With your partners, try to determine what prediction each of these students would make regarding the above experiment. Assume that each student continues to use the same line of reasoning as when discussing the block-and-spool problem.

Student 1:

Student 2:

Student 3:

Extended free-body diagram for spool A	Extended free-body diagram for spool B
(Point) free-body diagram for spool A	(Point) free-body diagram for spool B

Which student's reasoning, if any, is the same as what you used to make your prediction?

Can you use the outcome of this experiment to decide which line of reasoning about the block-and-spool problem is correct? If so, explain how. If not, explain why not.

⇨ Discuss your answers with a tutorial instructor before continuing.

E. Ask a tutorial instructor to provide you with the equipment you need to check your predictions. Ignore *small* differences in the motion of the spools.

How does the acceleration of the center of mass of spool A compare to that of spool B? Consider both magnitude and direction.

If necessary, describe how you would revise your free-body diagrams to be consistent with your observations.

F. Do the results of this experiment support the line of reasoning presented by student 1, student 2, or student 3? Explain.

G. Make the following generalizations on the basis of your observations:

If you want to determine how a force affects the motion of the center of mass of an object, should you consider:

• where on the object the force is exerted?

• how the force is affecting the rotational motion of the object?

H. Recall your prediction about the block-and-spool problem in section II. On the basis of your results thus far, was your prediction correct? If not, how can you resolve the inconsistency?

I. Energy analysis

You analyzed the block-and-spool problem and the falling-spools experiment in terms of forces. In the homework, you will be guided to consider these situations in terms of energy.

I. Interpreting center of mass

A. A T-shaped board of uniform mass density has two small holes as shown. Initially, the pivot is placed through the right hole, which corresponds to the *center of mass* of the board. The board is then held in place.

1. *Predict* the motion of the board after it is released from rest. Explain.

2. Check your prediction by observing the demonstration.

   a. Describe the angular acceleration of the board. Explain how you can tell.

      What does your answer imply about the *net torque* about the pivot? Explain.

   b. Describe the acceleration of the center of mass of the board. Explain how you can tell.

      What does your answer imply about the *net force* acting on the board? Explain.

3. Explain how your answers about net torque and net force in question 2 would change, if at all, if there is *appreciable friction* between the board and the pivot and the board remains at rest.

B. Imagine that the board is now hung from the hole to the left of the center of mass.

1. *Predict* the subsequent motion of the board after it is released. Explain.

2. On the diagram at right, draw and label an *extended free-body diagram* for the board just after it is released (*i.e.*, for each force, indicate explicitly a single point on the object at which the force can be regarded as acting).

   Explain how the diagram can be used to support your prediction for the motion of the board.

Extended free-body diagram for board

Tutorials in Introductory Physics
McDermott, Shaffer, and the P.E.G., U. Wash.

©Pearson
Custom 2nd Ed., for U.CO, Boulder

3. Obtain a T-shaped board and a pivot. Place the board on the pivot and check your predictions. Resolve any inconsistencies between your predictions and observations.

4. Place the board on the pivot with the center of mass directly above, directly below, and to the left of the pivot. Record your observations below.

An extended body can rotate freely about a fixed pivot if the friction between the object and the pivot is very small. A pivot that has negligible friction is sometimes referred to as a *frictionless pivot*. For all the following exercises and demonstrations in this tutorial, we will assume that the pivot is frictionless.

II. Applying the concept of center of mass

A. Attach clay to the bottom left side of the board so that it remains at rest when placed horizontally on the pivot. (The pivot should still be through the hole used in part B above.)

1. On the figure at right, mark the approximate location of the center of mass of the system composed of clay and board with an "x."

    Is the center of mass of the system located *to the left of, to the right of,* or *along* the vertical line through the pivot? Explain.

2. Suppose that the piece of clay were moved to a new location (point *A*) closer to the pivot.

    Predict whether the board would remain in equilibrium. Explain.

    Would the total mass to the left of the pivot change when the clay is moved to point *A?*

    Check your predictions.

Tutorials in Introductory Physics
McDermott, Shaffer, and the P.E.G., U. Wash.

©Pearson
Custom 2nd Ed., for U.CO, Boulder

3. Suppose the piece of clay were moved back to its original location and additional clay were added to it.

    Would the board remain in equilibrium? Explain.

    Is there any location along the bottom edge of the board at which this larger piece of clay could be placed so the board will be in equilibrium? If so, is the new location *closer to* or *farther from* the pivot?

    Check your prediction.

4. Generalize your observations from parts 1, 2, and 3:

    *   Is it possible to keep the total mass to either side of the pivot unchanged yet change the system so that it is no longer in equilibrium?

    *   Is it possible to change the *total mass* to one side of the pivot and still have the system in equilibrium?

    *   Is it enough to know the total mass to either side of the pivot in order to determine whether the system will be in equilibrium? Explain.

B. A student has balanced a hammer *lengthwise* on a finger. Consider the following dialogue between the student and a classmate.

    Student 1:   "The hammer is balanced because the center of mass is above my finger. The mass is the same on both sides of the center of mass—that is what the center of mass means."

    Student 2:   "It is not the mass, it is the torque that is the same for both parts of the hammer. If the torques weren't the same, the hammer would rotate."

    With which statements, if any, do you agree? Explain.

    Explain how one of the students above misinterpreted the term "center of mass."

In part A of section I you observed that the board will remain in equilibrium when placed on the pivot through its center of mass and released from rest. The figure at right shows the board with a vertical line through its center of mass.

Is the mass of the piece of board to the left of the dashed line *greater than*, *less than*, or *equal to* the mass of the piece of board to the right of the dashed line? Explain.

⇨ Obtain the necessary equipment from a tutorial instructor and check your answers. If necessary, resolve any inconsistencies. (*Hint:* Consider the areas of the pieces of board to the left and to the right of the pivot.)

C. Imagine that the T-shaped board (with no clay attached) were rotated as shown and then released from rest. The pivot passes through the center of mass of the board.

Frictionless pivot

1. *Predict* the subsequent motion of the board.

2. Check your prediction by watching the demonstration. Record your observation below.

3. What does your observation imply about the net torque about the pivot? Explain.

I. Angular momentum of a spinning wheel

Two students are initially at rest on stools that can rotate freely. Each student is then handed a bicycle wheel that is already spinning; the center of the wheel is stationary when it is given to the student. Assume that the wheel rotates freely on its axis.

In case A, the axle of the wheel is vertical as shown at right, and the wheel spins counterclockwise (as viewed from above).

In case B, the axle of the wheel is instead horizontal, and the top of the wheel moves away from the student as shown below right.

A. For each case, predict whether the student will *rotate clockwise*, *rotate counterclockwise*, or *remain at rest* (as viewed from above). Explain your reasoning.

Case A:

Case A:

Case B:

B. Observe the demonstration and check your predictions. If your observations differ from your predictions, record them below.

Case A:

Case B:

Case B

Just as a moving object has linear momentum, $\vec{p}$, a rotating object has *angular* momentum, $\vec{L}$.

As we will see, it is useful to treat angular momentum as having both a magnitude and a direction.

For an object that is symmetric about its axis of rotation, the angular momentum is parallel to the

axis of rotation. The orientation is determined using the *right hand rule:* when the fingers of the

right hand curl in the direction of the spin, the right thumb indicates the direction of $\vec{L}$.

C. For each case above, draw an arrow on the diagram that shows the direction of the angular momentum of the wheel at the instant shown.

D. On the basis of your observations thus far:

• Does any part of the spinning wheel move in the direction of the angular momentum?

• Does a wheel that is spinning and held in place appear to exert a force on its support in the direction of its angular momentum?

II. Angular momentum as a conserved vector quantity

A student sits at rest on a stool and holds a spinning bicycle wheel, as shown at right. Consider the following three separate experiments:

Experiment 1: The student places his arm against the side of the wheel, slowing it to half its initial angular speed.

Experiment 2: The student places his arm against the side of the wheel, bringing it to a stop.

Experiment 3: The student quickly flips the wheel over (so that it is spinning clockwise when viewed from above, with the *same* angular speed it had initially).

A. Predict whether the student will *rotate clockwise, rotate counterclockwise* or *remain at rest* at the end of each experiment. Explain.

B. Rank the three experiments according to *angular speed of the student at the end of the experiment,* from largest to smallest. If the final angular speed of the student is the same in any two experiments, state so explicitly. Explain.

C. Complete the angular momentum vector diagrams at right, where $\vec{L}_W$ and $\vec{L}_S$ are the angular momenta of the wheel and student, respectively.

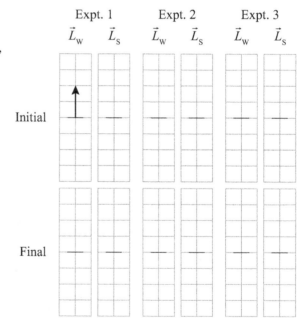

> Are your predictions above consistent with the results of your diagrams? If not, resolve the inconsistency.

D. How, if at all, would your predictions in part A differ if the direction of angular momentum were determined using the left hand instead of the right? Explain.

↻ Continue working through the tutorial. Before you leave class, return to part E below.

E. Observe the demonstration and check your predictions from part A. If your observations are different from your predictions, make a note of it.

> Is the ranking that you observed consistent with the assumption that the total angular momentum of the student-wheel system is constant? If not, resolve the inconsistency.

Tutorials in Introductory Physics
McDermott, Shaffer, and the P.E.G., U. Wash.

©Pearson
Custom 2nd Ed., for U.CO, Boulder

III. On-center and off-center collisions

Two collision experiments are performed with a puck and a rod on a level, low-friction air table. In each experiment: the puck moves with initial speed v_o and does not spin, the rod is initially at rest, and the puck sticks to the rod. The puck and rod have approximately equal masses.

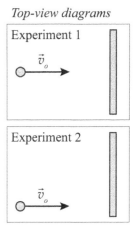

Top-view diagrams

In experiment 1, the puck moves toward the center of the rod.

In experiment 2, the puck moves toward a point near the end of the rod.

A. On each of the figures at right, label the (approximate) location of the center of mass of the puck-rod system at the instant shown.

B. Predict whether the final speed of the center of mass of the puck-rod system in experiment 1 will be *greater than, less than,* or *equal to* that in experiment 2. Explain your reasoning.

C. Two students discuss their predictions:

Student 1: "The system in experiment 1 will move across the table at a faster rate because the final momentum will be purely linear. In experiment 2, some of the initial linear momentum is converted into angular momentum when the puck and rod start spinning."

Student 2: "Both systems will move at the same speed because the initial linear momentum is the same in the two experiments. Linear momentum can't be turned into angular momentum—each kind of momentum is conserved separately."

With which student, if either, do you agree? Explain.

D. Ask a tutorial instructor for a series of photographs of the collision experiments described above.

1. Is the final speed of the center of mass of the puck-rod system in experiment 1 *greater than, less than,* or *equal to* that in experiment 2? Explain how you can tell from the photographs.

2. Do the photographs support the ideas presented by student 1 or student 2? Explain.

IV. Angular momentum of an object moving with constant velocity

The rod in the previous experiments is replaced by a disk as shown at right. In four different experiments, the center of the disk is placed at four different starting locations on the table: points *A*, *B*, *C*, and *D*. In all of these experiments, the puck has the same initial velocity and moves toward point *B*. The puck sticks to the disk in all cases.

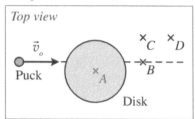

A. Two students discuss the results of the first experiment in which the disk is placed with its center on top of point *A* as shown at right:

Student 1: "After the collision, the puck and disk will spin, so there must be some final angular momentum. If the system has angular momentum after the collision, it must have it before the collision, since angular momentum is conserved."

Student 2: "That sounds reasonable, but how could there be initial angular momentum? There's nothing angular about an object moving in a straight line."

With which student, if either, do you agree? Explain.

In order to account for the rotational motion of the system after the collision in a way that is consistent with conservation of angular momentum, we will make the following assumptions:

• The puck somehow *does* have constant angular momentum before the collision.

• The manner in which the system spins *after* the collision can be used as an indicator of both the magnitude and direction of the angular momentum of the puck *before* the collision.

For example, if the manner in which the puck-disk system spins depends on whether the disk starts at point *A* or point *B*, we say that the angular momentum of the puck *with respect to* point *A* is different from the angular momentum of the puck *with respect to* point *B*.

B. Consider the angular momentum of the puck with respect to points *A*, *B*, *C*, and *D*. Points *C* and *D* are the same distance from the path of the puck.

Use the assumptions above to:

• Rank these angular momenta according to magnitude, from largest to smallest.

• Compare the directions of these angular momenta.

Tutorials in Introductory Physics
McDermott, Shaffer, and the P.E.G., U. Wash.

©Pearson
Custom 2nd Ed., for U.CO, Boulder

C. Now suppose that the puck has a different initial velocity. Its initial velocity is not given, but the puck moves such that:

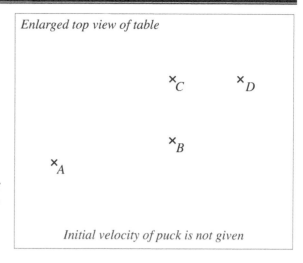

Enlarged top view of table

Initial velocity of puck is not given

- The angular momentum of the puck is the same with respect to points *A* and *B* in both magnitude and direction.

- The magnitude of the angular momentum of the puck is smaller with respect to point *A* than with respect to point *C*, and the directions of the angular momenta with respect to these points are opposite.

1. On the enlarged figure at right, sketch a path for the puck that satisfies the above conditions.

2. Label at least two new points with respect to which the angular momentum of the puck is the same as that with respect to point *C* in both magnitude and direction.

3. Compare your sketch with those drawn by other members of your group. Resolve any inconsistencies. If necessary, revise your sketch.

D. As you have seen, the angular momentum of an object depends on the point with respect to which it is measured. The magnitude of the angular momentum of a point object depends on the (shortest) distance from this reference point to the object's straight-line path. This distance is commonly referred to as $r_\perp$.

For each labeled point on the preceding two diagrams, draw and label $r_\perp$.

E. The magnitude of the angular momentum of point object Q with respect to point *W* is defined as $|\vec{L}_{QW}| = pr_\perp$, where p is the magnitude of the linear momentum of point object Q.

1. Explain how your answers to parts B and C are consistent with this formal definition of angular momentum.

2. Does the angular momentum of a point object moving with constant velocity *change* or *stay the same* as the object approaches a reference point?

Explain how your answer is consistent with this definition of angular momentum.

I.   Hooke's law for springs

A block of mass m on a frictionless surface is attached to an ideal massless spring, as shown in figure 1. The spring, which has spring constant k, is fixed to the wall. The dashed line indicates the position of the right edge of the spring when the spring is neither stretched nor compressed and the block is at its equilibrium position.

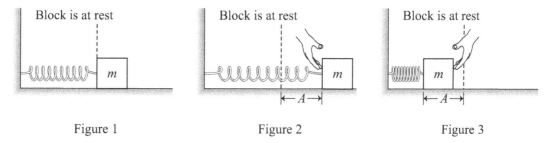

Figure 1   Figure 2   Figure 3

Figures 2 and 3 show the block held in place a distance A to the right and left of the equilibrium position, respectively.

A.   In the boxes at right, draw arrows to represent the directions of:

  • the position of the block, $\vec{x}$, taking $\vec{x} = \vec{0}$ when the block is at its equilibrium position and

  • the force on the block by the spring, $\vec{F}$.

Use the arrows that you drew to explain why the minus sign is necessary in the expression $\vec{F} = -k\vec{x}$ (Hooke's law for an ideal spring).

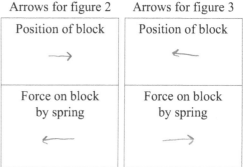

It is necessary to multiply the value of the spring constant by -1 because the vector direction of the force is dependent on the sign of the displacement and will always be in the opposing direction.

B.   What is the net force on the block when it is held in place as shown in figure 2? Explain.

The net force on the block in Figure 2 is zero. The force of the spring is in the leftward direction but the force of the hand is to the right and has an equal magnitude.

Suppose the hand in figure 2 were suddenly removed. After the hand is removed, how would the force on the block by the spring be related to the net force on the block? Explain.

If the hand were removed the force on the block by the spring would propel the block to the left past the point of equilibrium where the force would then change to the right. Because the table is frictionless the block would continue to oscillate in this pattern.

C.   Use Newton's second law to write an expression for the acceleration, $\vec{a}$, of the block in terms of $\vec{x}$, k, and m for an instant after the block has been released.

$ma = -kx$

$a = \dfrac{-kx}{m}$

II. Simple harmonic motion

A pendulum is hung directly above the block-spring system from section I. The block and the pendulum bob both have mass m. The spring constant is k, and the length of the pendulum is l. The parameters of the systems have been chosen such that the block is always directly below the pendulum bob.

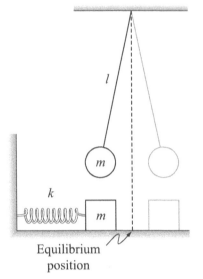

A. In the spaces below, draw a vector to represent the *net* force on each object when it is on the far left as shown.

Net force on block   Net force on bob

B. Suppose that the masses of the block and the pendulum bob were doubled, and the block and bob were then released from rest at the far left position.

The following questions serve as a guide to help you determine whether the block would remain directly below the pendulum bob at all times.

1. As a result of doubling the masses of the block and pendulum bob:

   Would the magnitude of the net force on each object when it is at the far left *increase by a factor of 2, decrease by a factor of 2*, or *remain the same?* Explain.

   - $F_{net, block}$

   - $F_{net, bob}$ The force on the pendulum would remain the same because

   Would the magnitude of the acceleration of each object when it is at the far left *increase by a factor of 2, decrease by a factor of 2*, or *remain the same?* Explain.

   - a_{block}

   - a_{bob}

   Would the time it takes each object to travel from the far left position to the equilibrium position, Δt_o, *increase, decrease,* or *remain the same?* Explain.

   - $\Delta t_{o, block}$

   - $\Delta t_{o, bob}$ The period of the pendulum would remain the same because the period is independent of the mass of the bob.

Tutorials in Introductory Physics
McDermott, Shaffer, and the P.E.G., U. Wash.

©Pearson
Custom 2nd Ed., for U.CO, Boulder

2. Check that your answers regarding Δt_o are consistent with the relationships below: *(Hint: For each object, what is the relationship between Δt_o and the period of oscillation, T?)*

- $T_{\text{block}} = 2\pi\sqrt{m/k}$ (period of oscillation for a mass on a spring)

- $T_{\text{bob}} = 2\pi\sqrt{l/g}$ (period of oscillation for a simple pendulum)

3. Will the block and pendulum bob still move together after their masses have been doubled? If not, describe what additional changes could be made so that the block and pendulum bob would again move together.

III. Energy of a simple harmonic oscillator

The diagram at right is a plot of the total energy of a horizontal block-spring system as a function of the position of the block with respect to its equilibrium position. The block oscillates with a maximum distance from equilibrium of A_o.

A. What feature of the diagram shows that the total energy of the system is *conserved* as the block oscillates?

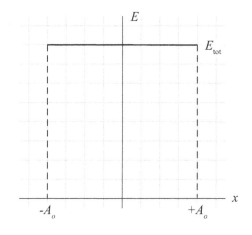

B. Determine what fraction of the total energy is potential energy when the block is at (1) $x = +A_o$ and (2) $x = +A_o/2$. *(Hint: $U = 1/2\ kx^2$.)*

On the same axes above, plot the potential energy stored in the spring, U, as a function of x. Your graph should correctly reflect your answers above.

C. On the same axes, plot the kinetic energy of the block, K, as a function of x. *(Hint: What function must be added to the potential energy to equal the total energy of the system?)*

Label your graphs so that you can easily distinguish the kinetic energy K from the potential energy U.

D. Is the time that the block takes to move from $x = 0$ to $x = +A_o/2$ *greater than, less than,* or *equal to* the time that the block takes to move from $x = +A_o/2$ to $x = +A_o$? Explain how your answer is consistent with your graph of the kinetic energy.

E. Consider two points, P and Q, to the right of the block's equilibrium position. Point P has position $x = +A_o/2$. Point Q is the point for which the kinetic energy and the potential energy of the system are each equal to half the total energy.

   1. Is point Q *to the left of, to the right of,* or *at the same position as* point P? Explain.

      Mark the locations of points P and Q on the x-axis above.

   2. When the block is at point P, is the kinetic energy of the system *greater than, less than,* or *equal to* the potential energy? Explain how you can tell from the graph.

   3. Calculate the ratio of the kinetic energy to the potential energy when the block is at point P (*i.e.*, at $x = +A_o/2$).

F. Suppose that the block were replaced by a block with half the mass and released from rest at $x = +A_o$.

   1. Describe any resulting changes in the three energy graphs (E_{total}, U, K). Explain.

   2. Is it possible to determine the period of oscillation of a mass-spring system using information from energy graphs alone? If so, describe the steps you would take to determine the period. If not, state what other information you would need.

G. Suppose instead that the original block were released from rest at $x = -A_o/2$ and moved between the positions $x = -A_o/2$ and $x = +A_o/2$.

1. As a result of this change, would the total energy *increase*, *decrease*, or *remain the same?* Explain.

2. On the axes at right, graph the total energy $E_{total, new}$, potential energy U_{new}, and kinetic energy K_{new} for the new motion.

3. Does any part of the new set of graphs exactly coincide with any part of the previous set of graphs? Explain.

4. Is the time that the block takes to move from $x = 0$ to $x = +A_o/2$ *greater than*, *less than*, or *equal to* the time that the block took to move from $x = 0$ to $x = +A_o/2$ *before* the amplitude of oscillation was reduced? Explain.

⇨ Check your answers with a tutorial instructor.

Electricity and magnetism

I. Electrical interactions

A. Press a piece of sticky tape, about 15–20 cm in length, firmly onto a smooth unpainted surface, for example, a notebook or an unpainted tabletop. (For ease in handling, make "handles" by folding each end of the tape to form portions that are not sticky.) Then peel the tape off the table and hang it from a support (*e.g.*, a wooden dowel or the edge of a table).

Describe the behavior of the tape as you bring objects toward it (*e.g.*, a hand, a pen).

B. Make another piece of tape as described above. Bring the second tape toward the first. Describe your observations.

It is important, as you perform the experiment above, that you keep your hands and other objects away from the tapes. Explain why this precaution is necessary.

How does the distance between the tapes affect the interaction between them?

C. Each member of your group should press a tape onto the table and write a *"B"* (for bottom) on it. Then press another tape on top of each B tape and label it *"T"* (for top).

Pull each pair of tapes off the table as a unit. After they are off the table, separate the T and B tapes. Hang one of the T tapes and one of the B tapes from the support at your table.

Describe the interaction between the following pairs of tape when they are brought near one another.

- two *T* tapes
- two *B* tapes
- a *T* and a *B* tape

Tutorials in Introductory Physics
McDermott, Shaffer, and the P.E.G., U. Wash.

©Pearson
Custom 2nd Ed., for U.CO, Boulder

D. Obtain an acrylic rod and a piece of wool or fur. Rub the rod with the wool, and then hold the rod near newly made *T* and *B* tapes on the wooden dowel.

Compare the interactions of the rod with the tapes to the interactions between the tapes in part C. Describe any similarities or differences.

We say that the rod and tapes are *electrically charged* when they interact as you have observed.

E. Base your answers to the following questions on the observations you have made thus far.

1. Is it possible that there is only one type of charge? If not, what is the minimum number of different types of charge needed to account for your observations thus far? Explain.

2. By convention, a glass rod is said to be "positively charged" when rubbed with silk. Your instructor will tell you whether your acrylic rod is positively or negatively charged when rubbed with the particular material you are using.

How do two objects that are positively charged interact? Explain how you can tell.

Which tape, *T* or *B*, has a positive charge? Explain.

↪ Discuss part I with a tutorial instructor before continuing.

Please remove all tape from the tabletop before continuing.

II. Superposition

Coulomb's law states that the electric force between two *point charges* acts along the line connecting the two points. (A *point charge* is a charged object that is sufficiently small that the charge can be treated as if it were all located at a single point.) The magnitude of the force on either of the charges is proportional to the product of the charges and is inversely proportional to the square of the distance between the charges.

Tutorials in Introductory Physics
McDermott, Shaffer, and the P.E.G., U. Wash.

©Pearson
Custom 2ⁿᵈ Ed., for U.CO, Boulder

A. Two positive point charges $+q$ and $+Q$ (with $|Q| > |q|$) are held in place a distance s apart.

1. Indicate the direction of the electric force exerted on each charge by the other.

2. Is the force on the $+q$ charge by the $+Q$ charge *greater than*, *less than*, or *equal to* the force on the $+Q$ charge by the $+q$ charge? Explain.

3. By what factor would the magnitude of the electric force on the $+q$ charge change if the charges were instead separated by a distance $2s$?

B. Two more $+Q$ charges are held in place the same distance s away from the $+q$ charge as shown. Consider the following student dialogue concerning the net force on the $+q$ charge:

Student 1: "The net electric force on the +q charge is now three times as large as before, since there are now three positive charges exerting forces on it."

Student 2: "I don't think so. The force from the +Q charge on the left will cancel the force from the +Q charge on the right. The net electric force will be the same as in part A."

1. Do you agree with either student? Explain.

2. Indicate the direction of the net electric force on the $+q$ charge. Explain.

3. What, if anything, can be said about how the magnitude of the net electric force on the $+q$ charge changes when the two $+Q$ charges are added? Explain.

C. Rank the four cases below according to the magnitude of the net electric force on the $+q$ charge. Explain how you determined your ranking.

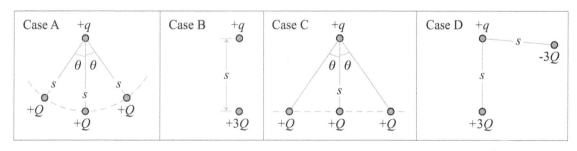

↪ Check your ranking with a tutorial instructor before continuing.

III. Distributed charge

A. Charge an acrylic rod by rubbing it with wool.

Obtain a small pith ball attached to an insulating thread. Touch the ball to the charged rod and observe the behavior of the ball after it touches the rod.

Is the ball charged after it touches the rod? If so, does the ball have the same sign charge as the rod or the opposite sign charge? Explain how you can tell.

B. Hold the charged rod horizontally. Use a charged pith ball to explore the region around the rod. On the basis of your observations, sketch a *vector* to represent the net electric force on the ball at each of the points marked by an "×."

Top view

Is all of the charge on the rod located at a single point? (*e.g.*, Is all the charge at the tip of the rod? At the middle?) Explain how you can tell.

On the basis of the vectors you have drawn, is it appropriate to consider the charged rod as a point charge? Explain.

C. Imagine that two charged rods are held together as shown and a charged pith ball is placed at point *P*.

Predict whether the rod farther from point *P* would exert an electric force on the pith ball. Explain.

× *P*

Top view

Check your prediction by placing a charged pith ball at point *P* near two charged rods and then slowly moving one rod away from the other. Describe your observations and discuss with your partners whether your results from this experiment support your prediction.

D. Five short segments (labeled 1–5) of acrylic rod are arranged as shown. All were rubbed with wool and have the same magnitude charge. A charged pith ball is placed in turn at the locations marked by points *A* and *B*.

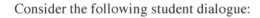

Top view

Indicate the approximate direction of the force on the pith ball at points *A* and *B* due to segment 5 alone.

What is the direction of the *net electric force* on the pith ball at points *A* and *B*? Explain how you determined your answer.

Does segment 2 exert a force on the pith ball when the pith ball is placed at point *B*? Explain.

E. In case A at right, a point charge $+q$ is a distance s from the center of a small ball with charge $+Q$.

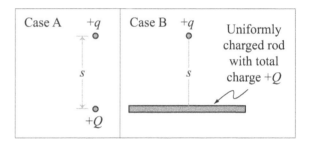

In case B the $+q$ charge is a distance s from the center of an acrylic rod with a total charge $+Q$.

Consider the following student dialogue:

Student 1: "The charged rod and the charged ball have the same charge, +Q, and are the same distance from the point charge, +q. So the force on +q will be the same in both cases."

Student 2: "No, in case B there are charges spread all over the rod. The charge directly below the point charge will exert the same force on +q as the ball in case A. The rest of the charge on the rod will make the force in case B bigger."

Neither student is correct. Discuss with your partners the errors made by each student. Write a correct description of how the forces compare in the space below. Explain.

IV. A model for electric charge

A. A small ball with zero net charge is positively charged on one side, and equally negatively charged on the other side. The ball is placed near a positive point charge as shown.

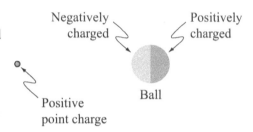

Would the ball be *attracted toward, repelled from,* or *unaffected by* the positive point charge? Explain.

Is your answer consistent with Coulomb's law? Explain.

B. Hang an uncharged metal or metal-covered ball from an insulating string. Then charge a piece of tape as in section I and bring the tape toward the ball.

Describe what you observe.

C. The situation in part A suggests a way to think about the attraction in part B between a charged piece of tape and an uncharged metal ball.

Try to account for the attraction in part B. As part of your answer, draw a sketch of the charge distribution on the tape and ball both before and after they are brought near one another.

I. Area as a vector

A. Hold a small piece of paper (*e.g.,* an index card) flat in front of you. The paper can be thought of as a part of a larger plane surface.

What *single* line could you use to specify the orientation of the plane of the paper (*i.e.,* so that someone else could hold the paper in the same, or in a parallel, plane)?

B. The area of a flat surface can be represented by a single *vector*, called the area vector, $\vec{A}$.

What does the direction of the vector represent?

What would you expect the magnitude of the vector to represent?

C. Place a large piece of graph paper flat on the table.

Describe the direction and magnitude of the area vector, $\vec{A}$, for the entire sheet of paper.

Describe the direction and magnitude of the area vector, $d\vec{A}$, for each of the individual squares that make up the sheet.

D. Fold the graph paper twice so that it forms a hollow triangular tube.

Can the entire sheet be represented by a single vector with the characteristics you defined above? If not, what is the minimum number of area vectors required?

E. Form the graph paper into a tube as shown.

Can the orientation of each of the individual squares that make up the sheet of graph paper still be represented by $d\vec{A}$ vectors as in part C above? Explain.

F. What must be true about a surface, or a portion of a surface, in order to be able to associate a single area vector $\vec{A}$ with that surface?

⇨ Discuss your responses with a staff member.

II. Electric field

A. In the tutorial *Charge*, you explored the region around a charged rod with a pith ball that had a charge of the same sign as the rod.

Side view

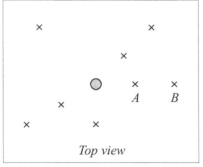

Top view

Sketch *vectors* at each of the marked points to represent the electric force exerted on the ball at that location.

How does the magnitude of the force exerted on the ball at point *A* compare to the magnitude of the force on the ball at point *B?*

B. Suppose that q_{test}, the charge on the pith ball, were halved.

Would the electric force exerted on the ball at each location change? If so, how? If not, explain why not.

Would the ratio $\vec{F}/q_{test}$ change? If so, how? If not, explain why not.

C. The quantity $\vec{F}/q_{test}$ evaluated at any point is called the *electric field* $\vec{E}$ at that point.

How does the magnitude of the electric field at point *A* compare to the magnitude of the electric field at point *B?* Explain.

D. Sketch *vectors* at each of the marked points to represent the electric field $\vec{E}$ at that location.

Would the magnitude or the direction of the electric field at point *A* change if:

• the magnitude of the charge on the *rod* were increased? Explain.

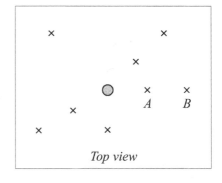

Top view

• the magnitude of the test charge were increased? Explain.

• the sign of the test charge were changed? Explain.

The electric field is typically represented in two ways: by *vectors* or by *electric field lines*. In the vector representation, vectors are drawn at various points to indicate the direction and magnitude of the electric field at those points. In the *field line* representation, straight or curved lines are drawn so that the tangent to each point on the line is along the direction of the electric field at that point. Below, we explore how the field line representation can also reflect the magnitude of the electric field.

E. The diagram at right shows a two-dimensional top view of the electric field lines representing the electric field for a positively charged rod.

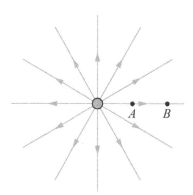

You determined previously that the magnitude of the electric field at point *A* was larger than the field at point *B*. What feature of the electric field lines reflects this information about the magnitude of the field?

⇨ Discuss your responses with a staff member.

III. Flux

Ask a tutorial instructor for a block of wood with nails through it. The nails represent uniform electric field lines. (The block of wood does not represent anything but serves to hold the nails in place.)

At right is a two-dimensional representation of the same electric field as viewed from the side.

A. Compare the magnitude of the electric field at points *P* and *Q*. Explain your reasoning.

Suppose you were given another block of wood with nails representing a weaker uniform electric field than the one above. How would the two blocks differ? Explain.

B. Obtain a wire loop. The loop represents the *boundary* of an imaginary flat surface of area *A*. (In order to allow the nails that represent the field to pass through the surface, you have been given only the boundary of the surface.)

Draw a diagram to show the relative orientation of the loop and the electric field so that the number of field lines that pass through the surface of the loop is:

• the maximum possible　　　　　　　　• the minimum possible

For a given surface, the *electric flux*, Φ_E, is proportional to the number of field lines through the surface. For a uniform electric field, the maximum electric flux is equal to the product of electric field at the surface and the surface area (*i.e., EA*). The electric flux is defined to be positive when the electric field $\vec{E}$ has a component in the same direction as the area vector $\vec{A}$ and is negative when the electric field has a component in the direction opposite to the area vector.

C. Sketch vectors $\vec{A}$ and $\vec{E}$ such that the electric flux is:

Positive	Negative	Zero

D. You will now examine the relationship between the number of field lines through a surface and the angle between $\vec{A}$ and $\vec{E}$.

(You will need a protractor to measure angles.)

1. Place the loop over the nails so that the number of field lines through it is a maximum. Determine the angle between $\vec{A}$ and $\vec{E}$. Record both that angle and the number of field lines that pass through the loop.

2. Rotate the loop until there is one fewer row of nails passing through it. Determine the angle between $\vec{A}$ and $\vec{E}$ and record your measurement. Continue in this way until $\theta = 180°$.

3. On graph paper, plot a graph of n versus θ. (Let the number of field lines through the surface be a negative number for angles between 90° and 180°.)

n (# of field lines through surface)	θ (angle between $\vec{A}$ and $\vec{E}$)

E. When $\vec{E}$ and $\vec{A}$ were parallel, we called the quantity EA the electric flux through the surface. For the parallel case, we found that EA is proportional to the number of field lines through the surface.

By what trigonometric function of θ must you multiply EA so that the product is proportional to the number of field lines through the area for any orientation of the surface?

Rewrite the quantity described above as a product of just the vectors $\vec{E}$ and $\vec{A}$.

Tutorials in Introductory Physics
McDermott, Shaffer, and the P.E.G., U. Wash.

©Pearson
Custom 2nd Ed., for U.CO, Boulder

I. Electric flux through closed surfaces

In the tutorial *Electric field and flux* and in the homework, we found that the electric flux through a set of imaginary surfaces, $d\vec{A}_i$, each with a uniform electric field, $\vec{E}_i$, can be written as:

$$\Phi_{net} = \vec{E}_1 \bullet d\vec{A}_1 + \vec{E}_2 \bullet d\vec{A}_2 + \vec{E}_3 \bullet d\vec{A}_3 + \ldots$$

The area vectors at each point on a *closed surface* (*i.e.,* a surface that surrounds a region so that the only way out of the region is through the surface) are chosen by convention to point *out of* the enclosed region. A closed imaginary surface is called a *Gaussian surface.*

In the following questions, a Gaussian cylinder with radius *a* and length *l* is placed in various electric fields. The end caps are labeled A and C and the side surface is labeled B. In each case, *base your answer about the net flux only on qualitative arguments about the absolute value of the flux through the end caps and side surface.*

A. The Gaussian cylinder is in a uniform electric field of magnitude E_o aligned with the cylinder axis.

  • Find the sign and absolute value of the flux through:

      Surface A: Surface B: Surface C:

  • Is the net flux through the Gaussian surface *positive, negative,* or *zero?*

B. The Gaussian cylinder encloses a negative charge. (The field from part A is removed.)

  • Find the sign of the flux through:

      Surface A: Surface B: Surface C:

  • Is the net flux through the Gaussian surface *positive, negative,* or *zero?*

C. The Gaussian cylinder encloses opposite charges of equal magnitude; the charges are on the axis of the cylinder and equidistant from the center.

  • Find the sign of the flux through:

      Surface A: Surface B: Surface C:

  • Is the net flux through the Gaussian surface *positive, negative,* or *zero?*

D. A positive charge is located above the Gaussian cylinder.

  • Find the sign of the flux through:

      Surface A: Surface B: Surface C:

  • Can you tell whether the net flux through the Gaussian surface is *positive, negative,* or *zero?* Explain.

⇨ Check your results with a tutorial instructor before continuing.

II. Gauss' law

Gauss' law states that the electric flux through a Gaussian surface is directly proportional to the net charge enclosed by the surface ($\Phi_E = q_{enclosed}/\varepsilon_o$).

A. Are your answers to parts A–C of section I consistent with Gauss' law? Explain.

B. In part D of section I, you tried to determine the sign of the flux through the Gaussian cylinder shown.

1. If you have not done so already, use Gauss' law to determine whether the net flux through the Gaussian surface is *positive*, *negative*, or *zero*. Explain.

2. If $\Phi_A = -10$ N-m^2/C and $\Phi_C = 2$ N-m^2/C, what is Φ_B?

C. Find the net flux through each of the Gaussian surfaces below.

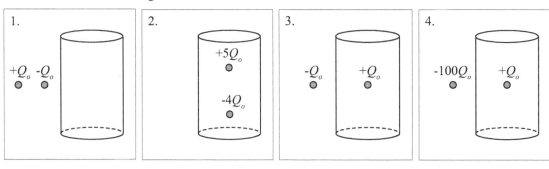

D. The three spherical Gaussian surfaces at right each enclose a charge $+Q_o$. In case C there is another charge $-6Q_o$ outside the surface.

Consider the following conversation:

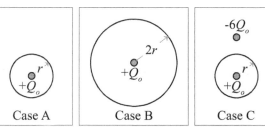

✓ Student 1: "Since each Gaussian surface encloses the same charge, the net flux through each must be the same."

✗ Student 2: "Gauss' law doesn't apply here. The electric field at the Gaussian surface in case B is weaker than in case A because the surface is farther from the charge. Since the flux is proportional to the electric field strength, the flux must also be smaller in case B."

✗ Student 3: "I was comparing A and C. In C the charge outside changes the field over the whole surface. The areas are the same, so the flux must be different."

Do you agree with any of the students? Explain.

III. Application of Gauss' law

A. A large sheet has charge density $+\sigma_o$. A cylindrical Gaussian surface encloses a portion of the sheet and extends a distance L_o on either side of the sheet. A_1, A_2, and A_3 are the areas of the ends and curved side, respectively. Only a small portion of the sheet is shown.

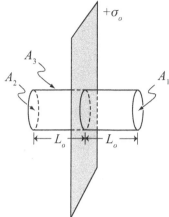

1. On the diagram at right indicate the location of the charge enclosed by the Gaussian cylinder.

   In terms of σ_o and other relevant quantities, what is the net charge enclosed by the Gaussian cylinder?

2. Sketch the electric field lines on both sides of the sheet.

   Does the Gaussian cylinder affect the field lines or the charge distribution? Explain.

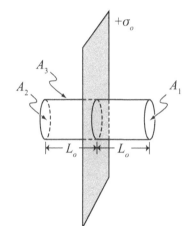

3. Let E_L and E_R represent the magnitudes of the electric field on the left and right ends of the Gaussian surface.

   How do E_L and E_R compare? Explain.

   How do the magnitudes of the areas of the ends of the Gaussian surface compare?

4. Through which of the surfaces (A_1, A_2, A_3) is there a net flux? Explain using a sketch showing the relative orientation of the electric field vector and the area vectors.

   Write an expression for the net electric flux Φ_{net} through the cylinder in terms of the three areas (A_1, A_2, A_3), E_L, and E_R.

   Use the relationships between the electric fields E_L and E_R and between the areas A_1 and A_2 to simplify your equation for the net flux.

5. Gauss' law ($\Phi_E = q_{enclosed}/\varepsilon_o$) relates the net electric flux through a Gaussian surface (which you found in part 4) to the net charge enclosed (which you found in part 1). Use this relationship to find the magnitude of the electric field at the right end of the cylinder in terms of σ_o.

What is the electric field at the left end of the cylinder?

Does the electric field near a large sheet of charge depend on the distance from the sheet? Use your results above to justify your answer.

Is your answer consistent with the electric field lines you sketched in part 2? Explain.

⇨ Check your results with a tutorial instructor before you continue.

B. The Gaussian cylinder below encloses a portion of two identical large sheets. The charge density of the sheet on the left is $+\sigma_o$; the charge density of the sheet on the right is $+2\sigma_o$.

1. Find the net charge enclosed by the Gaussian cylinder in terms of σ_o and any relevant dimensions.

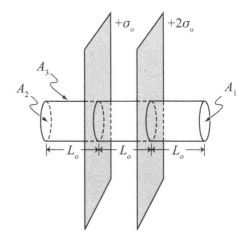

2. Let E_L and E_R be the magnitudes of the electric fields at the left and right end caps of the Gaussian cylinder respectively.

   Is E_L *greater than*, *less than*, or *equal to* E_R? Explain.

3. Find the net flux through the Gaussian cylinder in terms of E_L, E_R, and any relevant dimensions.

4. Use Gauss' law to find the electric field a distance L_o to the right of the rightmost sheet.

   Are your results consistent with the results you would obtain using superposition? Explain.

Tutorials in Introductory Physics
McDermott, Shaffer, and the P.E.G., U. Wash.

©Pearson
Custom 2nd Ed., for U.CO, Boulder

I. Review of work

A. Suppose an object moves under the influence of a force. Sketch arrows showing the relative directions of the force and displacement when the work done by the force is:

Positive	Negative	Zero

B. An object travels from point A to point B while two constant forces, $\vec{F}_1$ and $\vec{F}_2$, of equal magnitude are exerted on it.

1. Is the total work done on the object by $\vec{F}_1$ *positive, negative,* or *zero?*

2. Is the total work done on the object by $\vec{F}_2$ *positive, negative,* or *zero?*

3. Is the net work done on the object *positive, negative,* or *zero?* Explain.

4. Is the speed of the object at point B *greater than, less than,* or *equal to* the speed of the object at point A? Explain how you can tell.

C. An object travels from point A to point B while two constant forces, $\vec{F}_3$ and $\vec{F}_4$, of *unequal* magnitude are exerted on it as shown.

1. Is the total work done on the object by $\vec{F}_3$ *positive, negative,* or *zero?*

2. Is the total work done on the object by $\vec{F}_4$ *positive, negative,* or *zero?*

3. Is the net work done on the object *positive, negative,* or *zero?* Explain.

4. Is the speed of the object at point B *greater than, less than,* or *equal to* the speed of the object at point A? Explain how you can tell.

D. State the work-energy theorem in your own words. Are your answers in part B consistent with this theorem? Explain.

Are your answers in part C consistent with the work-energy theorem? Explain.

II. Work and electric fields

The diagram at right shows a top view of a positively charged rod. Points W, X, Y, and Z lie in a plane near the center of the rod. Points W and Y are equidistant from the rod, as are points X and Z.

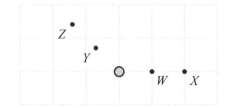

A. Draw electric field vectors at points W, X, Y, and Z.

B. A particle with charge $+q_o$ travels along a straight line path from point W to point X.

Is the work done *by the electric field* on the particle *positive, negative,* or *zero?* Explain using a sketch that shows the electric force on the particle and the displacement of the particle.

Compare the work done by the electric field when the particle travels from point W to point X to that done when the particle travels from point X to point W.

C. The particle travels from point X to point Z along the circular arc shown.

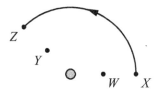

1. Is the work done *by the electric field* on the particle *positive, negative,* or *zero?* Explain. (*Hint:* Sketch the direction of the force on the particle and the direction of the displacement for several short intervals during the motion.)

Tutorials in Introductory Physics
McDermott, Shaffer, and the P.E.G., U. Wash.

©Pearson
Custom 2nd Ed., for U.CO, Boulder

2. Compare the work done by the electric field when the particle travels from point *W* to point *X* to that done when the particle travels from point *W* to point *Z* along the path shown. Explain.

D. Suppose the particle travels from point *W* to point *Y* along the path *WXZY* as shown.

1. Compare the work done by the electric field when the particle travels from point *W* to point *X* to that done when the particle travels from point *Z* to point *Y*. Explain.

What is the total work done on the particle by the electric field as it moves along the path *WXZY?*

2. Suppose the particle travels from *W* to *Y* along the arc shown. Is the work done on the particle by the electric field *positive, negative,* or *zero?* Explain using force and displacement vectors.

3. Suppose the particle travels along the straight path *WY*. Is the work done on the particle by the electric field *positive, negative,* or *zero?* Explain using force and displacement vectors. (*Hint:* Compare the work done along the first half of the path to the work done along the second half.)

E. Compare the work done as the particle travels from point W to point Y along the three different paths in part D.

It is often said that the work done by a static electric field is *path independent*. Explain how your results in part D are consistent with this statement.

III. Electric potential difference

A. Suppose the charge of the particle in section II is increased from $+q_o$ to $+1.7q_o$.

    1. Is the work done by the electric field as the particle travels from W to X *greater than, less than,* or *equal to* the work done by the electric field on the original particle? Explain.

    2. How is the quantity *the work divided by the charge* affected by this change?

The *electric potential difference* $\Delta V_{W \rightarrow X}$ in going from point W to point X is defined as:

$$\Delta V_{W \rightarrow X} = V_X - V_W \equiv -\frac{W_{\text{elec}}}{q}$$

where W_{elec} is the work done by the electric field on a charge q as it travels from point W to point X. [Note that some textbooks use different notation, *(e.g., ΔV_{WX}* rather than $\Delta V_{W \rightarrow X}$) or a different convention *(e.g., $\Delta V_{W \rightarrow X} = V_W - V_X$).* Check how your textbook expresses this relationship.]

    3. Does this quantity depend on the *magnitude* of the charge of the particle that is used to measure it? Explain.

    4. Does this quantity depend on the *sign* of the charge of the particle that is used to measure it? Explain.

B. Shown at right are four points near a positively charged rod. Points *W* and *Y* are equidistant from the rod, as are points *X* and *Z*. A charged particle with mass $m_o = 3 \times 10^{-8}$ kg is released from rest at point *W* and later is observed to pass point *X*.

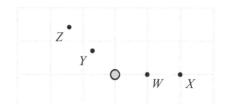

1. Is the particle positively or negatively charged? Explain.

2. Suppose that the magnitude of the charge on the particle is 2×10^{-6} C and that the speed of the particle is 40 m/s as it passes point *X*.

    a. Find the change in kinetic energy of the particle as it travels from point *W* to point *X*.

    b. Find the work done on the particle by the electric field between point *W* and point *X*. (*Hint:* See part D of section I.)

    c. Find the electric potential difference between point *W* and point *X*, $\Delta V_{W \to X}$ (*i.e.*, $V_X - V_W$).

    d. If the same particle were released from point *Y*, would its speed as it passes point *Z* be *greater than*, *less than*, or *equal to* 40 m/s? Explain.

3. Suppose that a second particle with the same mass as the first but nine times the charge (*i.e.*, 18×10^{-6} C) were released from rest at point *W*.

    a. Would the electric potential difference between points *W* and *X* change? If so, how, if not, why not?

    b. Would the speed of the second particle as it passes point *X* be *greater than*, *less than*, or *equal to* the speed of the first particle as it passed point *X*? Explain.

4. A particle with mass $m_o = 3 \times 10^{-8}$ kg is launched toward the rod from point Z and turns around at point Y.

    a. If the particle has charge $q_o = 2 \times 10^{-6}$ C, with what speed should it be launched? Explain.

    b. If instead the particle has charge $9q_o$ (*i.e.*, 18×10^{-6} C) with what speed should it be launched? Explain.

Tutorials in Introductory Physics
McDermott, Shaffer, and the P.E.G., U. Wash.

©Pearson
Custom 2nd Ed., for U.CO, Boulder

I. The electric field near conducting plates

A. A small portion near the center of a large thin conducting *plate* is shown magnified at right. The portion shown has a net charge Q_1 and each side has an area A_1.

Write an expression for the charge density on each side of the conducting plate.

Side view of thin charged plate

B. Use the principle of superposition to determine the electric field inside the conductor (if you have not done so already).

Is your answer consistent with your knowledge of the electric field inside a conductor? Explain.

C. Use the principle of superposition to determine the electric field to the left and to the right of the plate.

Does the charge on the *right* surface contribute to the electric field to the *left* of the plate (even though metal separates the two regions)? Explain.

Tutorials in Introductory Physics
McDermott, Shaffer, and the P.E.G., U. Wash.

©Pearson
Custom 2nd Ed., for U.CO, Boulder

D. Consider instead a portion near the center of a large *sheet* of charge. Like the plate in part A, the portion of the sheet has a net charge Q_1 and area A_1. The sheet, however, has negligible thickness.

How does the charge density σ' on this sheet compare to the charge density on each side of the plate above? Explain.

How does the electric field to one side of the *sheet of charge* (*e.g.,* to the left of the sheet of charge) compare to the electric field on the same side of the *charged plate?* Explain.

E. A second plate with the same magnitude charge as the first, but opposite sign, is now held near the first. The plates are large enough and close enough together that fringing effects near the edges can be ignored.

The diagrams below show various distributions of charge on the two plates. Decide which arrangement is physically correct. Explain.

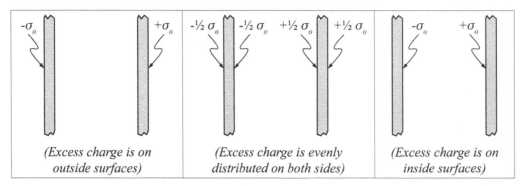

| (Excess charge is on outside surfaces) | (Excess charge is evenly distributed on both sides) | (Excess charge is on inside surfaces) |

II. Parallel plates and capacitance

Two very large thin conducting plates are a distance D apart. The surface area of the face of each plate is A_o. A side view of a small portion near the center of the plates is shown.

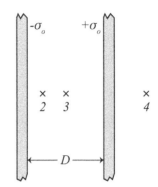

A. The inner surface of one plate has a uniform charge density of $+\sigma_o$; the other, $-\sigma_o$. The charge density on the outer surface of each plate is zero.

1. At each labeled point, draw vectors to represent the electric field at that point due to each charged plate.

2. Write expressions for the following quantities in terms of the given variables:

   • the electric field at points *1*, *2*, *3*, and *4*

   • the potential difference between the plates

3. The right plate is moved to the left as shown. Both plates are kept insulated. Describe how each of the following quantities will change (if at all). Explain.

   • the charge density on each plate

   • the electric field both outside and between the plates

   • the potential difference between the plates

4. Write expressions for the following quantities in terms of σ_o and d (the new distance between the plates).

  • the magnitude of the electric field between the plates

  • the potential difference between the plates

5. Find $\dfrac{Q}{\Delta V}$ (the ratio of the net charge on one plate to the potential difference between the plates).

   How, if at all, would this ratio change if the charge densities on the plates were $+2\sigma_o$ and $-2\sigma_o$?

⇨ Check your results for part A with a tutorial instructor before you continue.

B. Suppose the plates are discharged, then held a distance D apart and connected to a battery. (Ignore the fringing fields near the plate edges.)

  1. Write expressions for the following quantities in terms of the given variables. Explain your reasoning in each case.

    • the potential difference ΔV between the plates

    • the electric field at points *1*, *2*, *3*, and *4*

    • the charge density on each plate

2. The right plate is moved to the left. Describe how each of the following quantities changes (if at all). Explain.

    • the potential difference ΔV between the plates

    • the electric field both outside and between the plates

    • the charge density on each plate

3. Write expressions for the following quantities in terms of V_o and d (the new distance between the plates).

    • the magnitude of the electric field between the plates

    • the charge density on each plate

4. Find $\frac{Q}{\Delta V}$ (the ratio of the net charge on one plate to the potential difference between the plates).

    How, if at all, would this ratio change if the voltage of the battery was $2V_o$?

⇨   Check your results for part B with a tutorial instructor before you continue.

C. Compare the ratio $\frac{Q}{\Delta V}$ that you calculated for two insulated plates (part A) to the same ratio for two plates connected to a battery (part B).

1. Does the ratio $\frac{Q}{\Delta V}$ depend on whether or not the plates are connected to a battery?

2. Does the ratio $\frac{Q}{\Delta V}$ depend on the distance between the plates?

The potential difference ΔV between two isolated conductors depends on their net charges and their physical arrangement. If the conductors have charge $+Q$ and $-Q$, the ratio $\frac{Q}{\Delta V}$ is called the *capacitance (C)* of the particular arrangement of conductors.

D. For the following cases, state whether each of the quantities Q, σ, E, ΔV, and C changes or remains fixed:

1. two insulated conducting plates are moved farther apart

2. two conducting plates connected to a battery are moved farther apart

Tutorials in Introductory Physics
McDermott, Shaffer, and the P.E.G., U. Wash.

©Pearson
Custom 2nd Ed., for U.CO, Boulder

In this tutorial, we construct a model for electric current that we can use to predict and explain the behavior of simple electric circuits.

I. Complete circuits

A. Obtain a battery, a light bulb, and a single piece of wire. Connect these in a variety of ways. Sketch each arrangement below.

Arrangements that *do* light the bulb	Arrangements that *do not* light the bulb

You should have found at least four different arrangements that light the bulb. How are these arrangements similar? How do they differ from arrangements in which the bulb does not light?

State the requirements that must be met in order for the bulb to light.

B. A student has briefly connected a wire across the terminals of a battery until the wire feels warm. The student finds that the wire seems to be equally warm at points *1, 2,* and *3.*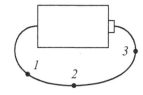

Based on this observation, what might you conclude is happening in the wire at one place compared to another?

Tutorials in Introductory Physics
McDermott, Shaffer, and the P.E.G., U. Wash.

©Pearson
Custom 2nd Ed., for U.CO, Boulder

C. Light a bulb using a battery and a single wire. Observe and record the behavior (*i.e.,* brightness) of the bulb when objects made out of various materials are inserted into the circuit. (Try materials such as paper, coins, pencil lead, eraser, your finger, *etc.*)

What is similar about most of the objects that let the bulb light?

D. Carefully examine a bulb. Two wires extend from the filament of the bulb into the base. You probably cannot see into the base, however, you should be able to make a good guess as to where the wires are attached. Describe where the wires attach. Explain based on your observations in parts A–C.

On the basis of the observations that we have made, we will make the following assumptions:

1. A flow exists in a complete circuit from one terminal of the battery, through the rest of the circuit, back to the other terminal of the battery, through the battery and back around the circuit. We will call this flow *electric current*.

2. For identical bulbs, bulb brightness can be used as an indicator of the amount of current through that bulb: the brighter the bulb, the greater the current.

Starting with these assumptions, we will develop a model that we can use to account for the behavior of simple circuits. The construction of a scientific model is a step-by-step process in which we specify only the minimum number of attributes that are needed to account for the phenomena under consideration.

Tutorials in Introductory Physics
McDermott, Shaffer, and the P.E.G., U. Wash.

©Pearson
Custom 2nd Ed., for U.CO, Boulder

II. Bulbs in series

Set up a two-bulb circuit with identical bulbs connected one after the other as shown. Bulbs connected in this way are said to be connected in *series*.

A. Compare the brightness of the two bulbs with each other. (Pay attention only to large differences in brightness. You may notice minor differences if two "identical" bulbs are, in fact, not quite identical.)

Use the assumptions we have made in developing our model for electric current to answer the following questions:

1. Is current "used up" in the first bulb, or is the current the same through both bulbs?

2. Do you think that switching the order of the bulbs might make a difference? Check your answer.

3. On the basis of your observations *alone*, can you tell the direction of the flow through the circuit?

B. Compare the brightness of each of the bulbs in the two-bulb series circuit with that of a bulb in a single-bulb circuit.

Use the assumptions we have made in developing our model for electric current to answer the following questions:

1. How does the current through a bulb in a single-bulb circuit compare with the current through the same bulb when it is connected in series with a second bulb? Explain.

2. What does your answer to question 1 imply about how the current through the *battery* in a single-bulb circuit compares to the current through the *battery* in a two-bulb series circuit? Explain.

C. We may think of a bulb as presenting an obstacle, or *resistance*, to the current in the circuit.

    1. Thinking of the bulb in this way, would adding more bulbs in series cause the total obstacle to the flow, or *total resistance*, to increase, decrease, or stay the same as before?

    2. Formulate a rule for predicting how the current through the battery would change (*i.e.*, whether it would *increase, decrease,* or *remain the same*) if the number of bulbs connected in series were increased or decreased.

III. Bulbs in parallel

Set up a two-bulb circuit with identical bulbs so that their terminals are connected together as shown. Bulbs connected together in this way are said to be connected in *parallel*.

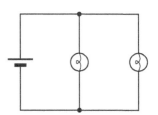

A. Compare the brightness of the bulbs in this circuit.

    1. What can you conclude from your observation about the amount of current through each bulb?

    2. Describe the current in the entire circuit. Base your answer on your observations. In particular, how does the current through the battery seem to divide and recombine at the junctions of the two parallel branches?

B. Is the brightness of each bulb in the two-bulb parallel circuit *greater than, less than,* or *equal to* that of a bulb in a single-bulb circuit?

How does the amount of current through a *battery* connected to a single bulb compare to the current through a *battery* connected to a two-bulb parallel circuit? Explain based on your observations.

C. Formulate a rule for predicting how the current through the battery would change (*i.e.,* whether it would *increase, decrease,* or *remain the same)* if the number of bulbs connected in parallel were increased or decreased. Base your answer on your observation of the behavior of the two-bulb parallel circuit and the model for current.

What can you infer about the total resistance of a circuit as the number of parallel branches is increased or decreased?

D. Does the amount of current through a battery seem to depend on the number of bulbs in the circuit and how they are connected?

E. Unscrew one of the bulbs in the two-bulb parallel circuit. Does this change significantly affect the current through the branch that contains the other bulb?

A characteristic of an *ideal* battery is that the branches connected directly across it are independent of one another.

IV. Limitations: The need to extend the model

A. The circuit at right contains three identical bulbs and an ideal battery. Assume that the resistance of the switch, when closed, is negligible. Use the model we have developed to:

 • predict the relative brightness of the bulbs in the circuit with the switch closed. Explain.

 • predict how the brightness of bulb A changes when the switch is opened. Explain.

B. Show that a simple application of the model for current that we have developed thus far is inadequate for determining how the brightness of bulb B changes when the switch is opened.

Tutorials in Introductory Physics
McDermott, Shaffer, and the P.E.G., U. Wash.

©Pearson
Custom 2nd Ed., for U.CO, Boulder

Previously, we have developed a model to account for the behavior of simple circuits in which bulb brightness can be used as an indicator of the amount of current through that bulb. In this tutorial, we extend this model to include the concept of potential difference.

I. Review: Current and resistance

The circuits at right contain identical batteries and bulbs. The boxes labeled X and Y represent different unknown elements. (Assume there are no batteries in either box.)

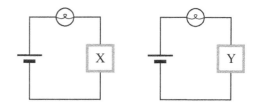

It is observed that the bulb on the left is brighter than the bulb on the right.

A. Based on this observation, is the resistance of element X *greater than*, *less than*, or *equal to* that of element Y? Explain.

B. In each circuit, is the current through the bulb *greater than*, *less than*, or *equal to* the current through the unknown element?

C. In each circuit, is the current through the bulb *greater than*, *less than*, or *equal to* the current through the battery?

II. Batteries in series

Ask a tutorial instructor for the circuits shown at right.

Observe the relative brightness of the bulbs.

Circuit I   Circuit II   Circuit III

A. Rank the bulbs according to *current through each bulb*, from largest to smallest. If the current through any two bulbs is the same, state so explicitly. Explain how you can tell without using an ammeter.

B. Is the current through battery D *greater than*, *less than*, or *equal to* the current through battery A? Explain how you can tell.

Tutorials in Introductory Physics
McDermott, Shaffer, and the P.E.G., U. Wash.

©Pearson
Custom 2nd Ed., for U.CO, Boulder

C. Is the current through battery B *greater than, less than,* or *equal to* the current through battery A? Explain how you can tell.

If a battery were added to a circuit in series, would the current through the circuit *increase, decrease,* or *remain the same?* Explain.

The above observations suggest that we may think of a battery as the agent that "pushes" or "drives" current through a circuit. We explore this relationship in greater detail below.

III. Potential difference

A. Use a voltmeter to measure the absolute value of the potential difference across each element in circuits I–III (reproduced at right). Record your measurements in the table provided.

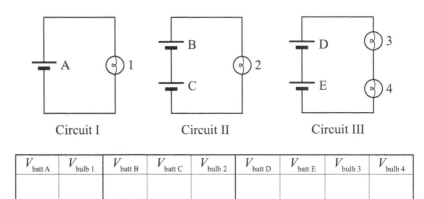

Circuit I   Circuit II   Circuit III

$V_{batt A}$	$V_{bulb 1}$	$V_{batt B}$	$V_{batt C}$	$V_{bulb 2}$	$V_{batt D}$	$V_{batt E}$	$V_{bulb 3}$	$V_{bulb 4}$

B. Rank the bulbs according to *absolute value of the potential difference across the bulb,* from largest to smallest. (Ignore any small differences.)

How does the ranking of the bulbs according to potential difference compare to that according to brightness?

The observations above suggest that we can extend our model for electric circuits to include the idea that, for circuits containing identical bulbs, the brightness of a bulb is not only an indicator of the current through a bulb but also an indicator of the potential difference across it.

Tutorials in Introductory Physics
McDermott, Shaffer, and the P.E.G., U. Wash.

©Pearson
Custom 2nd Ed., for U.CO, Boulder

C. *Predict* what the voltmeter would read if it were connected across the network of batteries D and E. Explain your reasoning.

Use a voltmeter to check your predictions. Resolve any inconsistencies.

D. *Predict* what the voltmeter would read if it were connected across the network of bulbs 3 and 4. Explain your reasoning.

Check your predictions, and resolve any inconsistencies.

E. Use your observations to devise a rule that relates the potential difference across a network of circuit elements that are connected in series to the potential difference across each of the elements in the network.

F. Consider circuits II and IV, shown at right.

1. *Predict* the ranking of the bulbs according to brightness, from brightest to dimmest. If any of the bulbs will have the same brightness, state so explicitly. Explain.

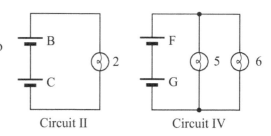

Circuit II   Circuit IV

Ask a tutorial instructor for these circuits so that you can check your ranking. Resolve any inconsistencies.

2. *Predict* the ranking of the bulbs according to *absolute value of the potential difference across the bulb*, from largest to smallest. If the potential difference across any two bulbs will be the same, state so explicitly. Explain.

Is your ranking of the bulbs according to potential difference consistent with that according to brightness?

Use a voltmeter to check your predictions. Resolve any inconsistencies.

3. Is the current through battery F *greater than, less than,* or *equal to* the current through battery B? Explain.

G. Answer the following questions on the basis of your work so far:

1. If two *bulbs* have the same potential difference across them, do they necessarily have the same current through them? Explain.

2. If two *batteries* have the same potential difference across them, do they necessarily have the same current through them? Explain.

⇨ Discuss your responses to part G with a tutorial instructor.

IV. Circuits with multiple loops

A. Consider circuit V, shown at right. Predict what a voltmeter would read if it were connected across each of the elements in this circuit. Explain.

Circuit V

$V_{\text{batt H}}$	$V_{\text{batt I}}$	$V_{\text{bulb 7}}$	$V_{\text{bulb 8}}$	$V_{\text{bulb 9}}$

Obtain this circuit from an instructor, and check your predictions. If your measurements are not consistent with your prediction, resolve the inconsistencies.

B. Consider circuit VI, shown at right. Rank the bulbs according to *absolute value of the potential difference across the bulb,* from largest to smallest. Explain.

Circuit VI

Obtain this circuit from an instructor, and measure the voltage across each circuit element. If your measurements are not consistent with your ranking, resolve the inconsistencies.

$V_{\text{batt J}}$	$V_{\text{batt K}}$	$V_{\text{bulb 10}}$	$V_{\text{bulb 11}}$	$V_{\text{bulb 12}}$

Tutorials in Introductory Physics
McDermott, Shaffer, and the P.E.G., U. Wash.

©Pearson
Custom 2nd Ed., for U.CO, Boulder

C. Circuits V and VI (reproduced at right) each have more than one path for the current.

Circuit V   Circuit VI

1. On each circuit diagram at right, sketch all possible current loops that go through the two-battery network.

2. For each current loop that you have drawn, calculate the sum of the absolute values of the potential differences across the bulbs in that loop. (Use the measurements you made above.)

3. How does the sum of the absolute values of the potential differences across the bulbs in each loop compare to the absolute value of the potential difference across the two-battery network in that loop?

V. Generalizations: Potential difference across networks

Networks N, O, and P, each of which consists of two or more identical bulbs, are connected to a battery as shown.

A. How is the potential difference across network N related to that across the battery? Explain.

B. How are the potential differences across networks O and P related to that across the battery? Explain.

C. Suppose that network O consists of bulbs that are connected in series. How is the potential difference across network O related to the potential difference across each bulb? Explain.

D. Suppose instead that network P consists of bulbs that are connected in parallel. How is the potential difference across network P related to the potential difference across each bulb? Explain.

Throughout this tutorial, when you are asked to *predict* the behavior of a circuit, do so *before* setting up the circuit.

I.   Simple RC circuits

A. A capacitor is connected to a battery, bulb, and switch as shown. Assume that the switch has been closed for an *extended period of time*.

1. *Predict* whether the brightness of the bulb is *the same as, greater than,* or *less than* the brightness of a single bulb connected to a battery. Explain.

2. *Predict* how the potential difference across the battery compares to the potential difference across the capacitor plates and to the potential difference across the bulb. Explain.

3. Briefly describe the distribution of charge, if any, on the capacitor plates.

   Recall the relationship between the charge on a capacitor and the potential difference across the capacitor. Use this relationship to describe how you could use a voltmeter to determine the charge on a capacitor.

4. Obtain the circuit and a voltmeter. Check your predictions for parts 1 and 2.

B. Remove the capacitor and the bulb from the circuit.

   1. *Predict* the potential difference across the bulb and the potential difference across the capacitor while these elements are disconnected from the circuit and from each other. Explain.

   Check your prediction.

   2. *Predict* whether the potential difference across the capacitor will *increase, decrease,* or *remain the same* if a wire is connected from "ground" to one or the other of the terminals of the capacitor. Explain your reasoning.

   Check your prediction. (You can use a wire with clip leads connected to a metal table leg as a "ground.")

   3. Devise and carry out a method to reduce the potential difference across the capacitor to zero. (This is sometimes called *discharging* the capacitor.)

   4. The capacitor in part A is said to be *charged* by the battery.

   Does the capacitor have a *net* charge after being connected to the battery?

   In light of your answer above, what is meant by *the charge* on a capacitor?

II. Charging and discharging capacitors

A. Suppose an uncharged capacitor is connected in series with a battery and bulb as shown.

1. *Predict* the behavior of the bulb when the switch is closed. Explain.

   Set up the circuit and check your prediction. If your prediction is in conflict with your observation, how can you account for your observation?

2. *Without using a voltmeter*, determine the potential difference across the capacitor at the following times:

   • *just after* the switch is closed. Explain how you can tell. (*Hint:* Compare the brightness of the bulb to the brightness of a bulb connected to a battery in a single-bulb circuit without a capacitor.)

   • *a long time after* the switch is closed. Explain how you can tell.

   Use a voltmeter to check your predictions. (*Hint:* Be sure to discharge the capacitor completely after each observation.)

B. Suppose that instead of connecting the uncharged capacitor to the single bulb A, you connected it to the two-bulb circuit shown at right.

1. *Predict* how the *initial brightness* of bulb B compares to the initial brightness of bulb C. Explain.

2. *Predict* how the *initial brightness* of bulb B compares to the initial brightness of bulb A above. Explain.

   Discharge the capacitor and then set up the circuit with the uncharged capacitor and check your predictions. If your prediction is in conflict with your observation, how can you account for your observation?

3. *Predict* how the final charge on the capacitor compares to the final charge on the capacitor from part A.

Use a voltmeter to check your prediction.

C. Suppose that the bulbs were connected in parallel, rather than in series.

1. *Predict* how the *initial brightness* of bulb D compares to the initial brightness of bulb E. Explain.

2. *Predict* how the *initial brightness* of bulb D compares to the initial brightness of bulbs A, B, and C above. Explain.

3. *Predict* how the final charge on the capacitor compares to the final charge on the capacitor from part A. Explain.

Set up the circuit and check your predictions. If your prediction is in conflict with your observation, how can you account for your observation?

D. After completing the experiments above, two students make the following comments:

Student 1: "The capacitor with two bulbs in series got charged up a lot more than the capacitor with two bulbs connected in parallel because the series circuit charged the capacitor for a longer period of time."

Student 2: "I disagree, the bulbs in the parallel circuit were brighter so this capacitor gained more charge."

Do you agree with student 1, student 2, or neither? Explain your reasoning.

E. Suppose that a different capacitor of smaller capacitance were connected to the battery and a single bulb in series.

    1. *Predict* how the initial potential difference across the bulb compares to the initial potential difference across the bulb in part A.

    2. *Predict* how the initial brightness of the bulb compares to the brightness of the single bulb in part A. Explain.

    3. *Predict* how the final amount of charge on the capacitor would compare to the final amount of charge on the capacitor from part A.

        Set up the circuit and check your predictions. If your prediction is in conflict with your observation, how can you account for your observation?

III. Multiple capacitors

A bulb is connected to a battery and two capacitors as shown at right. Suppose that C_1 is less than C_2.

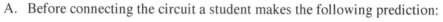

A. Before connecting the circuit a student makes the following prediction:

    "Current flows from the positive side of the battery to the negative side of the battery. Since the bulb is isolated from the battery on both sides by the capacitors, the bulb will not light."

Do you agree or disagree with this prediction? Explain.

        Obtain a second capacitor from your instructors and check your prediction.

B. Make the following predictions on the basis of your observations of this circuit. Do not use a voltmeter.

   1. Just after the switch is closed:

      • What is the potential difference across the bulb? Explain how you can tell from the brightness of the bulb.

      • What is the potential difference across each of the capacitors? Explain your reasoning.

   2. A long time after the switch is closed:

      • What is the potential difference across the bulb? Explain how you can tell.

      • What is the sum of the potential differences across the two capacitors? Explain.

      • Is the final charge on capacitor 1 *greater than, less than,* or *equal to* the final charge on capacitor 2? Explain.

      • Is the potential difference across capacitor 1 *greater than, less than,* or *equal to* the potential difference across capacitor 2? Explain.

   Use the voltmeter to check your predictions in part B.

I. Magnetic materials

A. Investigate the objects that you have been given (magnets, metals, cork, plastic, wood, *etc.*). Separate the objects into three classes based on their interactions with each other.

1. List the objects in each of your classes.

   <u>Class 1</u>   <u>Class 2</u>   <u>Class 3</u>

2. Fill out the table below with a word or two describing the interaction between members of the same and different classes.

   Table of interactions

	Class 1	Class 2	Class 3
Class 1			
Class 2			
Class 3			

3. Are all metals in the same class?

4. To which class do magnets belong? Are all the objects in this class magnets?

B. Obtain a permanent magnet and an object that is attracted to the magnet but not repelled. Imagine that you do not know which object is the magnet. Using only these two objects, find a way to determine which object is the permanent magnet. (*Hint:* Are there parts on either object that do not interact as strongly as other parts?)

C. The parts of a permanent magnet that interact most strongly with other materials are called the *poles* of a magnet.

   How many magnetic poles does each of your magnets have? Explain how you found them.

   How many different *types* of poles do you have evidence for so far? Explain.

   Using three magnets, find a way to distinguish one *type* of pole from another.

D. Describe how an *uncharged* pith ball suspended from a string can be used to test whether an object is charged.

    Predict what will happen when an uncharged pith ball is brought near one of the poles of the magnet. Explain.

    Obtain a pith ball and test your prediction. Record your results.

    Based on your observations above, *predict* what will happen when the pith ball is brought near the other pole of the magnet. Test your prediction.

    Is there a *net charge* on the north (or south) pole of a magnet? Explain.

E. A paper clip is attached to a string and suspended from a straw. It is then placed so that it hangs as shown inside a cup lined with aluminum foil.

    1. *Predict* what will happen to the paper clip when a charged rod is brought near the cup. Explain in terms of the electric field inside the aluminum-lined cup.

Aluminum-lined cup

Paper clip

        Obtain the equipment and test your prediction.
        Discuss this experiment with your partners.

        Predict what you would observe if the paper clip were outside the cup. Explain your reasoning, then check your prediction.

    2. Bring a magnet near the cup and observe what happens to the paper clip inside the cup. Record your observations.

F. Based on your observations in parts D and E above, would you say that a magnetic interaction is the *same as* or *different from* an electrical interaction? Explain.

II. Magnetic fields

We have observed that magnets interact even when they are not in direct contact. In electrostatics we used the idea of an electric field to account for the interaction between charges that were separated from one another. For magnetic interactions, we similarly define a *magnetic field*.

A. Obtain a compass from a tutorial instructor.

1. Use the compass to explore the region around a bar magnet.

   Describe the behavior of the compass needle both near the poles of the magnet and in the region between the poles.

   To which class of objects from section I does the compass needle belong? Explain.

2. Move the compass far away from all other objects. Shake the compass and describe the behavior of the compass needle.

   Does the needle behave as if it is in a magnetic field?

   We can account for the behavior of the compass needle by supposing that it interacts with the Earth and that the Earth belongs to one of the categories from section I.

   To which class of objects from section I do your observations suggest the Earth belongs? Explain how you can tell.

3. We define the *north pole* of a magnet as the end that points toward the arctic region of the Earth when the magnet is free to rotate and is not interacting with other nearby objects.

   On the basis of this definition, is the geographic north pole of the Earth a magnetic north pole or a magnetic south pole?

   Use your compass to identify the north pole of an unmarked bar magnet.

B. Place a bar magnet on an enlargement of the diagram at right.

1. Place the compass at each of the lettered points on the enlargement and draw an arrow to show the direction in which the north end of the compass points.

   Discuss with your partners how the interaction of the compass with the magnet depends on the distance from the bar magnet and the location around the bar magnet.

   Devise a method by which you can determine the approximate relative magnitudes of the magnetic field at each of the marked locations. Explain your reasoning.

2. We *define* the direction of the magnetic field at a point as the direction in which the north end of a compass needle points when the compass is placed at that point.

   Make the arrows on your enlargement into magnetic field *vectors* (*i.e.*, draw them so that they include information about both the magnitude and direction of the field).

C. Obtain some small magnets and stack them north-to-south until you have a bar about the same length as your bar magnet. Place them on an enlargement of the diagram at right.

1. On the enlargement, sketch the magnetic field *vectors* at the locations *A–E*.

   How does the magnetic field of the stack of magnets compare to the magnetic field of the bar magnet?

2. Break the stack in half and investigate the breaking points. Describe how many north and how many south poles result.

   What does your observation suggest about how a bar magnet would behave when broken in half?

3. On your enlargement draw the magnetic field vectors at the six locations *A–F* when just the right half of the stack of magnets is present.

Using a different color pen, draw the magnetic field vectors when just the left half of the stack of magnets is present.

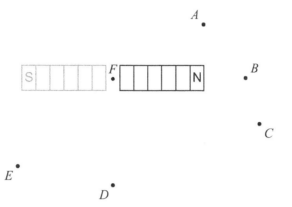

Compare the field vectors for the two half-stacks of magnets to the field vectors for the whole stack.

Is your observation consistent with the idea that magnetic fields obey the principle of superposition? Explain.

From your observations, what can you infer about the direction of the magnetic field inside a bar magnet? Explain.

Sketch magnetic field vectors for a few points inside the magnet.

Does the magnetic field of a bar magnet always point away from the north pole and toward the south pole of the magnet? Explain.

What can you infer about the strength of the magnetic field inside the magnet as compared to outside the magnet?

I. The magnetic force on a current-carrying wire in a magnetic field

Obtain the following equipment:

- magnet
- wooden dowel
- ring stand and clamp
- battery
- two paper clips
- two alligator-clip leads
- 30 cm piece of connecting wire
- magnetic compass
- enlargement showing magnet and wire

Hang the connecting wire from the paper clips as shown so that it swings freely. Do not connect the wires to the battery until told to do so.

A. On an enlargement of the figure below, sketch field lines representing the magnetic field of the bar magnet. Show the field both inside and outside the magnet.

On the diagram, indicate the direction of the current through the wire when the circuit is complete.

Predict the direction of the force exerted on the wire by the magnet when the circuit is complete. Explain.

Check your prediction. (Do not leave the battery connected for more than a few seconds. The battery and wires will become hot if the circuit is complete for too long.)

B. Make predictions for the following five situations based on what you observed in part A. Check your answers only after you have made all five predictions.

1. The magnet is turned so that the south pole is near the wire while the battery is connected.

   Prediction:

   Observation:

2. The leads to the battery are reversed (consider both orientations of the magnet).

   Prediction:

   Observation:

3. The north pole of the magnet is held near the wire but the battery is not connected.

   Prediction:

   Observation:

4. The north pole of the magnet is held: (a) closer to the wire and (b) farther from the wire.

   Prediction:

   Observation:

5. The magnet is turned so that it is parallel to the wire while the battery is connected.

   Prediction:

   Observation:

Resolve any discrepancies between your predictions and your observations. (*Hint:* Consider the *vector* equation for the magnetic force on a current-carrying wire in a uniform magnetic field: $\vec{F} = i\vec{L} \times \vec{B}$.)

II. The magnetic field of a current-carrying wire

A. Suppose you place a small magnet in a magnetic field and allow it to rotate freely. How will the magnet orient relative to the external magnetic field lines? Illustrate your answer below.

B. Suppose you hold a magnetic compass near a current-carrying wire as shown. (A *magnetic compass* is a magnet that can rotate freely.) The face of the compass is parallel to the tabletop.

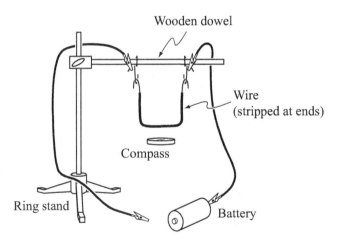

   1. *Predict* the orientation of the compass needle when the circuit is complete. Sketch a diagram that shows the wire, the direction of the current through it, the direction of the magnetic field directly below the wire, and the predicted orientation of the compass needle.

   2. Check your answer. If the deflection of the needle is not what you predicted, resolve the discrepancy. (*Hint:* Is there more than one magnetic field affecting the compass?)

C. Now suppose that you hold the compass at some other locations near the wire (*e.g.*, directly above the wire or to one side of a vertical wire). For each location, *predict* the orientation of the compass needle when the circuit is closed. Make sketches to illustrate your predictions.

Check your answers. If the orientation of the compass needle is not what you predicted, resolve the discrepancy.

D. Sketch the magnetic field lines of a current-carrying wire. Include the direction of the current in the wire in your sketch.

III. Current loops and solenoids

A. A wire is formed into a loop and the leads are twisted together. The sides of the loop are labeled A–D. The direction of the current is shown. (The diagram uses the convention that $\odot$ indicates current out of the page and $\otimes$ indicates current into the page.)

Plane of cross-section

Cross-section at center of loop (seen from side C)

1. On the top two diagrams at right, sketch magnetic field lines for the loop. Base your answer on your knowledge of the magnetic field of a current-carrying wire.

   Explain why it is reasonable to ignore the effect of the magnetic field from the wire leads.

2. Consider the magnetic field of a bar magnet.

   How are the magnetic field lines for the current loop similar to those for a short bar magnet?

   Can you identify a "north" and a "south" pole for a current loop?

   Devise a rule by which you can use your right hand to identify the magnetic poles of the loop from your knowledge of the direction of the current.

B. A small current loop is placed near the end of a large magnet as shown.

   1. Draw vectors to show the magnetic force on each side of the loop.

       What is the net effect of the magnetic forces exerted on the loop?

   2. Suppose that the loop were to rotate until oriented as shown.

       Now, what is the net effect of the magnetic forces exerted on the loop?

       Is there an orientation for which there is no net torque on the loop? Draw a diagram to illustrate your answer.

   3. Are your results above consistent with regarding the current loop as a small magnet? Label the poles of the current loop in the diagrams above and check your answer.

C. A solenoid is an arrangement of many current loops placed together as shown below. The current through each loop is the same and is in the direction shown.

Obtain or draw an enlargement of the figure.

1. At each of the labeled points, draw a vector to indicate the direction and magnitude of the magnetic field. Use the principle of superposition to determine your answer.

2. Sketch magnetic field lines on the enlargement.

Describe the magnetic field near the center of the solenoid.

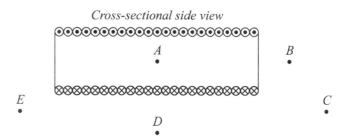

Cross-sectional side view

3. How does the field of the solenoid at points *A–E* compare with that of a bar magnet (both inside and outside)?

Which end of the solenoid corresponds to a north pole? Which end corresponds to a south pole?

4. How would the magnetic field at any point within the solenoid be affected by the following changes? Explain your reasoning in each case.

• The current through each coil of the solenoid is increased by a factor of two.

• The number of coils in each unit length of the solenoid is increased by a factor of two, with the current through each coil remaining the same.

I. Induced currents

A. A copper wire loop is placed in a uniform magnetic field as shown. Determine whether there would be a current through the wire of the loop in each case below. Explain your answer in terms of magnetic forces exerted on the charges in the wire of the loop.

- The loop is stationary.

- The loop is moving to the right.

- The loop is moving to the left.

B. Suppose that the loop is now placed in the magnetic field of a solenoid as shown.

1. Determine whether there would be a current through the wire of the loop in each case below. If so, give the direction of the current. Explain in terms of magnetic forces exerted on the charges in the wire of the loop.

   - The loop is stationary.

   - The loop is moving toward the solenoid.

   - The loop is moving away from the solenoid.

2. For each case above in which there is an induced current, determine:

   - the direction of the *magnetic moment* of the loop. (*Hint:* Find the direction of the magnetic field at the center of the loop due to the induced current in the loop. The magnetic moment is a vector that points in this same direction.)

   - whether the loop is *attracted toward* or *repelled from* the solenoid.

   - whether the force exerted on the loop tends to *increase* or to *decrease* the relative motion of the loop and solenoid.

Tutorials in Introductory Physics
McDermott, Shaffer, and the P.E.G., U. Wash.

©Pearson
Custom 2nd Ed., for U.CO, Boulder

C. In each of the diagrams below, the position of a loop is shown at two times, t_o and $t_o + \Delta t$. The loop starts from rest in each case and is displaced to the right in case A and to the left in case B. On the diagrams indicate:

- the direction of the induced current through the wire of the loop,

- the magnetic moment of the loop,

- an area vector for each loop,

- the sign of the flux due to the external magnetic field (at both instants), and

- the sign of the induced flux (at both instants).

 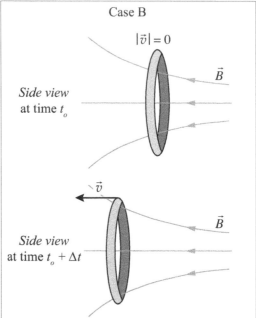

D. State whether you agree or disagree with each of the students below. If you agree, explain why. If you disagree, cite a specific case for which the student's statement does not give the correct answer. (*Hint:* Consider cases A and B above.)

Student 1: "The magnetic field due to the loop always opposes the external magnetic field."

Student 2: "The flux due to the loop always has the opposite sign as the flux due to the external magnetic field."

Student 3: "The flux due to the loop always opposes the change in the flux due to the external magnetic field."

⇨ Before continuing, check your answers to parts C and D with a tutorial instructor.

II. Lenz' law

A. The diagram at right shows a stationary copper wire loop in a uniform magnetic field. The magnitude of the field is *decreasing* with time.

1. Would you predict that there would be a current through the loop:

   • if you were to use the idea that there is a magnetic force exerted on a charge moving in a magnetic field? Explain your reasoning.

   • if you were to use the reasoning of the student in part D of section I with whom you agreed? Explain.

2. It is *observed* that there is an induced current through the wire loop in this case. Use the appropriate reasoning above to find the direction of the current through the wire of the loop.

To understand the interaction between the wire loops and solenoids in section I, we can use the idea that a force is exerted on a charged particle moving in a magnetic field. In each of those cases, there was an induced current when there was relative motion between the solenoid and the wire loop. In other situations such as the one above, however, there is an induced current in the wire loop even though there is no relative motion between the wire loop and the solenoid. There is a general rule called *Lenz' law* that we can use in *all* cases to predict the direction of the induced current.

B. With your partners, discuss the statement of Lenz' law in your textbook. Make sure you understand how it is related to the statement by the student with whom you agreed in part D of section I.

C. A wire loop moves from a
region with no magnetic
field into a region with a
uniform magnetic field
pointing into the page.

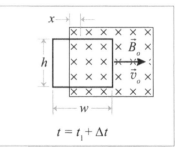

The loop is shown at two
instants in time, $t = t_1$ and
$t = t_1 + \Delta t$.

1. Is the magnetic flux through the loop due to the external field *positive*, *negative*, or *zero*:

   • at $t = t_1$?

   • at $t = t_1 + \Delta t$?

2. Is the *change* in flux due to the external field during the interval Δt *positive*, *negative*, or *zero*?

3. Use Lenz' law to determine whether the flux due to the induced current in the loop is *positive*, *negative*, or *zero*.

4. What is the direction of the current in the loop during this time interval?

D. At two later instants, $t = t_2$
and $t = t_2 + \Delta t$, the loop is
located as shown.

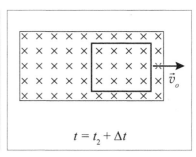

1. Use Lenz' law to determine whether the flux due to the current induced in the loop is *positive*, *negative*, or *zero*. Explain.

2. Describe the current in the loop during this time interval.

3. Consider the following student dialogue:

   Student 1: "The sign of the flux is the same as it was in part C. So the current here will also be counter-clockwise."

   Student 2: "I agree. If I think about the force on a positive charge on the leading edge of the loop, it points towards the top of the page. That's consistent with a counter-clockwise current."

   Do you agree with either student? Explain.

I. Faraday's law

Two loops of the same radius are held near a solenoid. Both loops are the same distance from the end of the solenoid and are the same distance from the axis of the solenoid.

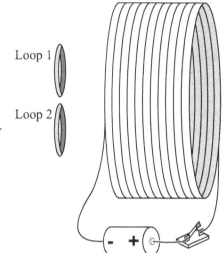

A. The resistance of loop 2 is greater than that of loop 1. (The loops are made from different materials.)

1. Is there a current induced through the wire of either of the loops:

   • before the switch is closed? Explain.

   • just after the switch is closed? Explain.

   • a long time after the switch is closed? Explain.

2. For the period of time that there is a current induced through the wire of the loops, find the direction of the current.

3. The ratio of the induced currents for the two loops is found by experiment to be equal to the inverse of the ratio of the resistances of the loops.

   What does this observation imply about the ratio of the induced emf in loop 1 to that in loop 2?

B. Suppose that loop 2 were replaced by a wooden loop.

   • Would there still be an emf in the loop?

   • Would there still be a current induced in the wood loop?

C. Suppose that loop 2 were removed completely. Consider the circular path that the wire of loop 2 used to occupy.

   • Would there still be an emf along the path? Explain.

   • Would there still be a current along the path? Explain.

The results of the previous exercises are consistent with the idea that a change in the magnetic flux through the surface of a loop results in an *emf* in that loop. If there is a conducting path around the loop (*e.g.*, a wire), there will be a current. The emf is independent of the material of which the loop is made; the current is not. It is found by experiment that the induced emf is proportional to the rate of change of the magnetic flux through the loop. This relationship is called *Faraday's law*. The direction of any induced current is given by Lenz' law.

D. Three loops, all made of the same type of wire, are placed near the ends of identical solenoids as shown. The solenoids are connected in series. Assume that the magnetic field near the end of each of the solenoids is uniform.

Loop 2 consists of two turns of a single wire that is twice as long as the wire used to make loop 1. Loop 3 is made of a single wire that is half as long as the wire used to make loop 1.

Just after the switch is closed, the current through the battery begins to increase. The following questions concern the period of time during which the current is increasing.

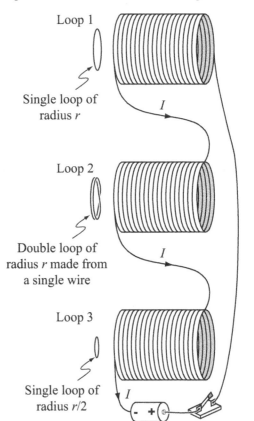

1. Let $\mathcal{E}$ represent the induced emf in loop 1. Find the induced emf in each of the other loops in terms of $\mathcal{E}$. Explain your reasoning.

2. Let R represent the resistance of loop 1. Find the resistance of each of the other loops in terms of R. Explain.

3. Find the current induced through the wire of each of the loops in terms of $\mathcal{E}$ and R.

II. Applications

A. *Galvanometer*

Obtain a device like the one shown below. It contains a coil made of many loops of wire and a magnet suspended so that it is free to swing. A pointer has been attached to the magnet so that a small swing of the magnet will result in a large deflection of the pointer. When there is no current through the coil, the magnet is horizontal and the pointer is vertical.

Predict the deflection of the pointer (if any) when the switch is closed. Explain the reasoning you used to make your prediction.

Connect the circuit and observe the deflection of the pointer. If your observation is in conflict with your prediction, discuss your reasoning with a tutorial instructor.

The device above is called a *galvanometer* and can be used to detect current. If the scale on the galvanometer has been calibrated to measure amperes, the device is called an *ammeter*.

B. *Simple electric motor*

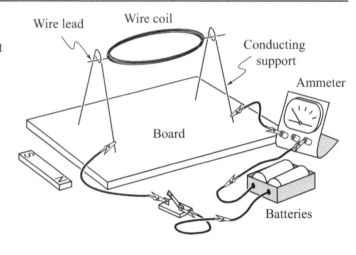

Obtain the equipment illustrated at right and assemble it as shown.

You should have:

- a magnet, a battery, a switch, some connecting wire, and an ammeter.

- a copper wire coil. The ends of the wire leads to the coil have been stripped of the insulating enamel coating so that half the wire is bare.

- two conducting supports for the leads to the coil.

1. Examine the leads to the wire coil closely, so that you understand which portion of the wire has been stripped of the insulating coating.

   For what orientations of the coil will there be a current through it due to the battery?

Wire lead half stripped of insulating coating

Check your answer by closing the switch and observing the deflection of the ammeter as you rotate the coil manually through one complete revolution.

2. Hold one pole of the magnet near the coil. Close the switch. If the coil does not begin to spin, adjust the location of the magnet or gently rotate the coil to start it spinning.

   Use the ideas that we have developed in this and previous tutorials to explain the motion of the wire coil. (The questions that follow may serve as a guide to help you develop an understanding of the operation of the motor.)

Tutorials in Introductory Physics
McDermott, Shaffer, and the P.E.G., U. Wash.

©Pearson
Custom 2nd Ed., for U.CO, Boulder

3. When the coil is in the position shown, there is a current, *I*, through it.

*View of end of wire lead
(insulation has been stripped
from lower half)*

a. The coil is manually started spinning so that it rotates clockwise.

During which portions of the cycle does the coil form a complete circuit with the battery such that there is a current through the wire of the coil?

The current results in a magnetic moment that interacts with the magnetic field of the magnet. Will the interaction tend to *increase* or to *decrease* the angular speed of the coil? Explain.

b. The coil is manually started spinning so that it rotates counterclockwise:

During which portions of the cycle does the coil form a complete circuit with the battery so that there is a current through the wire of the coil?

The current results in a magnetic moment that interacts with the magnetic field of the magnet. Will the interaction tend to *increase* or to *decrease* the angular speed of the coil? Explain.

Check that the behavior of your motor is consistent with your answers.

4. Consider the following questions about the motor:

• Why was insulated wire used for the coil? Would bare wire also work? Explain.

• Would you expect the motor to work if the leads to the coil were stripped completely? Explain.

5. Predict the effect on the motor of (i) reversing the leads to the battery and (ii) reversing the orientation of the magnet.

Check your predictions.

C. *Electric generator*

Remove the battery and ammeter
from the circuit in part B and
insert a micro-ammeter as shown.

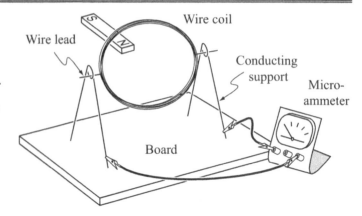

1. Suppose that the coil is made
    to spin by an external agent
    such as yourself.

    Predict the deflection of the
    micro-ammeter needle
    throughout a complete
    revolution of the coil.

How would your prediction change if:

• the coil were made to rotate the other way?

• the poles of the magnet were reversed?

2. Check your predictions by gently rotating the coil so that it spins for a little time on its
    own before coming to a stop.

When the coil of the apparatus above is made to spin by an external agent, the apparatus is

called an *electric generator*.

Waves

I. Pulses on a spring

A tutorial instructor will demonstrate various pulses on a stretched spring. Observe the motion of the pulse and of the spring in each case and discuss your observations with your classmates.

A. A piece of yarn has been attached to the spring. How did the motion of the yarn compare to the motion of the pulse for each type of pulse that you observed?

The terms *transverse* or *longitudinal* are often used to describe the types of pulses you have observed in the demonstration. To what feature of a pulse do these terms refer?

For the rest of this tutorial we will focus on *transverse* pulses along the spring.

B. During the demonstration, did any of the following features change *significantly* as a pulse moved along the spring? (Ignore what happens when a pulse reaches the end of the spring.)

*   the amplitude of the pulse

*   the width of the pulse

*   the shape of the pulse

*   the speed of the pulse

C. During the demonstration, each of the following quantities was changed. Did any of the changes significantly affect the speed of the pulse? If so, how?

*   the tension (*e.g.*, by stretching the spring to a greater length)

*   the amplitude of the pulse

*   the width of the pulse

*   the shape of the pulse

II. Superposition

A. The snapshots below show two pulses approaching each other on a spring. The pictures were taken at equal time intervals. The pulses are on the "same side" of the spring (*i.e.*, each displaces the spring toward the top of the page).

1. When the pulses meet, does each pulse continue to move in the direction it was originally moving, or does each reverse direction?

   Give evidence from the photos to support your answer.

2. When the pulses completely overlap, as shown in snapshot 5, how does the shape of the disturbance in the spring compare to the shapes of the individual pulses?

3. Describe how you could use the *principle of superposition* to determine the shape of the spring at any instant while the pulses "overlap."

4. Two pulses (1 and 2) approach one another as shown. The bottom diagram shows the location of pulse 1 a short time later.

   In the space at right, sketch the location of pulse 2 at this later time. On the same diagram, sketch the shape of the spring at this instant in time.

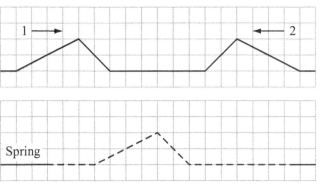

Tutorials in Introductory Physics
McDermott, Shaffer, and the P.E.G., U. Wash.

©Pearson
Custom 2nd Ed., for U.CO, Boulder

B. Two pulses of equal width and equal amplitude approach each other on *opposite sides* of a spring (*i.e.*, the pulses displace the spring in opposite directions). The snapshots below were taken at equal time intervals.

1. Is the behavior of the spring consistent with the principle of superposition? If so, which quantity is "added" in this case? If not, explain why not.

2. Below is a simplified representation of both individual pulses at a time between the instants shown in snapshots 4 and 5.

   Sketch the shape of the spring at the instant shown.

3. Let point Q be the point on the spring midway between the pulses, as shown.

   Describe the motion of point Q during the time interval shown.

4. Which, if any, of the following changes would affect the motion of point Q? Explain.

   • doubling the amplitude of both pulses

   • doubling the amplitude of just one pulse

   • doubling the width of just one pulse

5. Consider an *asymmetric* pulse as shown.

   What shape would a second pulse need to have in order that point Q not move as the two pulses pass each other?

   On the diagram, indicate the shape, location, and direction of motion of the second pulse at the instant shown.

   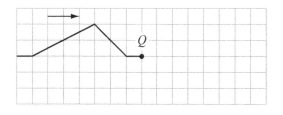

III. Reflection

A. *Reflection from a fixed end*

The snapshots at right show a pulse being *reflected* from the end of a spring that is held fixed in place.

1. Describe the similarities and differences between the *incident pulse* (the pulse moving toward the fixed end) and the *reflected pulse*.

2. Consider the situation in part B of section II, in which two pulses on opposite sides of a spring meet. Use a piece of paper to cover the right half of those photographs so that the portion of the spring *to the left of point Q* is uncovered.

   How does the behavior of the uncovered portion of the spring (including point *Q*) compare to the behavior of the spring shown at right?

The results of the exercise above suggest a model for the reflection of pulses from fixed ends of springs. We imagine that the spring extends past the fixed end and that we can send a pulse along the imaginary portion toward the fixed end. We choose the shape, orientation, and location of the imaginary pulse so that, as it passes the incident pulse, the end of the spring *remains fixed*. (Such a condition that governs the behavior of the end of the spring is an example of a *boundary condition*.) In this case, the reflected and imaginary pulses have the same shape and orientation.

3. A pulse with speed 1.0 m/s is incident on the fixed end of a spring.

   Determine the shape of the spring at (a) $t = 0.2$ s, (b) $t = 0.4$ s, and (c) $t = 0.6$ s.

   How does the shape of the reflected pulse compare to that of the incident pulse?

(1 square = 10 cm)   Fixed end

B. *Reflection from a free end*

Before you leave class, observe a demonstration of a pulse reflecting from the *free end* of a spring. Record your observations. You will investigate this situation in the homework

I. Pulses on a spring

A student creates a pulse on a stretched spring by moving one end of the spring along the y-axis. The student's hand starts at $y = 0$ m. At $t = t_1$, it begins to move in the positive y-direction until it reaches $y = y_o$, then it returns to $y = 0$ m at $t = t_2$. The shape of the spring a short time later, at $t = t_3$, is shown at right.

A. Imagine that you measure the time it takes the pulse to pass point P (*i.e.*, you measure the time interval that begins when the leading edge of the pulse reaches point P and ends when the trailing edge passes point P).

Is this time interval *greater than, less than,* or *equal to* the time it took to generate the pulse (*i.e.*, $t_2 - t_1$)? Explain.

B. In a second experiment, the student stretches the spring even more, so that the propagation speed doubles. The student then moves the end of the spring in exactly the same way as in the first experiment.

1. Compare the distances traveled by the leading edges of the pulses in the two experiments during the interval from t_1 to t_3.

2. Is the width of the pulse in experiment 2 *greater than, less than* or *equal to* the width of the pulse in experiment 1? Explain.

3. On the diagram at right, draw the shape of the spring at time t_3 in experiment 2. (The dashed line shows shape of the spring at time t_3 in experiment 1.) Make sure that your sketch is consistent with your answers above.

Experiment 2

4. Is the time it takes for the pulse in experiment 2 to pass point P *greater than, less than,* or *equal to* the time it took to generate the pulse (*i.e.*, $t_2 - t_1$)? Explain.

C. What *single* change could the student make to experiment 1 to create a narrower pulse?

Is more than one answer possible? Explain.

⇨ Check your answers to this section with a tutorial instructor.

Tutorials in Introductory Physics
McDermott, Shaffer, and the P.E.G., U. Wash.

©Pearson
Custom 2nd Ed., for U.CO, Boulder

II. Reflection and transmission at a boundary

The photographs below illustrate the behavior of two springs joined end-to-end when a pulse reaches the boundary between the springs. The snapshots were taken at equal time intervals.

A. Describe what happens after the pulse reaches the boundary between the springs.

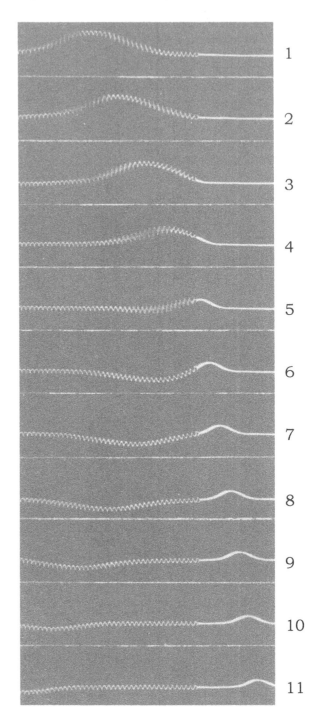

Compare the widths of the incident and transmitted pulses.

B. Compare the speed of a pulse in one spring to the speed of a pulse in the other spring. Make this comparison in two ways:

1. Use the information contained in two or more snapshots. Explain.

2. Use the information contained in only a single snapshot (*e.g.*, snapshot 8). Explain.

C. In answering the questions below, assume that each spring has approximately uniform tension.

1. How does the tension in one spring compare to the tension in the other spring? Explain.

2. How does the linear mass density, μ, of one spring compare to the linear mass density of the other? Explain.

⇨ Check your answers with a tutorial instructor.

III. Transmission of multiple pulses

Suppose two identical pulses are sent toward the boundary between the two springs from section II, as illustrated below. For this part of the tutorial, ignore reflected pulses.

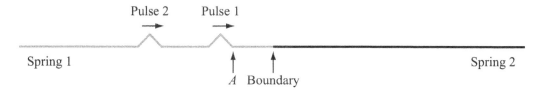

A. Imagine that you measure the time interval Δt_1 that begins when the leading edge of pulse 1 reaches point A and ends when the leading edge of pulse 2 reaches that same point.

Would this time interval be different if you chose point A to lie at another location along spring 1? Explain.

B. The diagram below represents the instant when the leading edge of pulse 1 reaches the boundary.

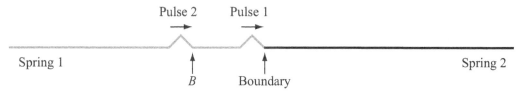

Is the time that it will take for the leading edge of pulse 2 to travel from point B to the boundary *greater than, less than,* or *equal to* Δt_1? Explain.

C. On the diagram below, sketch a possible location of pulse 1 on spring 2 at the instant when the leading edge of pulse 2 reaches the boundary.

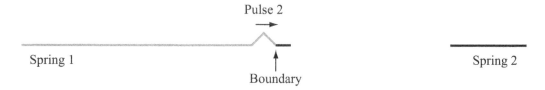

Label the location of the leading edge of pulse 1 as point C.

Is the time it took for pulse 1 to travel from the boundary to point C *greater than, less than,* or *equal to* Δt_1? Explain.

Would the distance between the transmitted pulses be *greater than, less than,* or *equal to* the distance between the incident pulses? Explain.

D. Would the time interval Δt_1 that you measured in part A for the pulses traveling on spring 1 be *greater than*, *less than*, or *equal to* the corresponding time interval for the transmitted pulses on spring 2?

E. Is the time it takes a single incident pulse to pass point *A greater than*, *less than*, or *equal to* the time it takes a single transmitted pulse to pass point *C?*

Explain how the change in the width of the pulse as it passes from the first spring to the second is a direct consequence of the difference in speed in the two springs.

⇨ Check your answers for parts A through E with a tutorial instructor.

IV. Reflection and transmission at a boundary revisited

The springs in the photograph at right are the same as in the photographs in section II. However, now a pulse approaches the boundary between the springs from the right.

A. Predict whether there would be a reflected pulse after the trailing edge of the incident pulse has reached the boundary.

If so: On which side of the spring will the reflected pulse be located? How will its width compare to the width of the incident pulse?

If not: Explain why not.

How will the transmitted pulse compare to the incident pulse?

In the space below the photograph, make a sketch that shows the shape of the springs at an instant after the incident pulse is completely transmitted. Your sketch should illustrate the relative widths of the pulse(s) and their relative distance(s) from the boundary as well as the side of the spring on which each pulse is traveling.

B. Ask a tutorial instructor for a time sequence of photographs that illustrates this situation so that you can check your predictions.

If your prediction was incorrect, identify those parts of your prediction that were inconsistent with the photographs.

Tutorials in Introductory Physics
McDermott, Shaffer, and the P.E.G., U. Wash.

©Pearson
Custom 2nd Ed., for U.CO, Boulder

V. A model for reflection at a boundary

We have observed that reflection occurs when a pulse reaches the boundary between two springs, that is, where there is an abrupt *change* in medium. We would like to be able to predict whether the boundary will act more like a fixed end or more like a free end.

A. In the situation illustrated in section II, are the incident and reflected pulses on the *same* side of the spring, or are they on *opposite* sides of the spring?

On the basis of this observation, does it appear that the reflection at the boundary is more like that from a *fixed end* or that from a *free end?*

B. Which of the following quantities are different on the two sides of the boundary?

- tension

- linear mass density

- wave speed

Which of the above quantities could you use to predict whether the boundary will act more like a fixed end or more like a free end? (It may help to consider limiting cases, *i.e.*, very large or very small values of the properties.)

Describe how you could predict whether the reflected pulse will be on the same side of the spring as the incident pulse or whether it will be on the opposite side.

Describe how you could predict whether the transmitted pulse will be on the same side of the spring as the incident pulse or whether it will be on the opposite side.

C. Imagine that a pulse on a spring is approaching a boundary. Would the boundary act more like a fixed end or more like a free end if the spring is connected to:

- a very massive chain?

- a very light fishing line?

I. Water waves in regions of different depths

Shown at right is a side-view diagram of part of a large tank of water containing two regions of different depths.

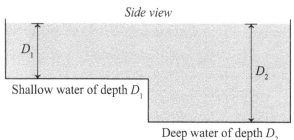

Side view

D_1

Shallow water of depth D_1

D_2

Deep water of depth D_2

It is observed that water waves travel *more quickly* in deep water than in shallow water.

A periodic wave is generated on the left side of the tank. (The wave is not shown.)

A. When the periodic wave crosses the boundary, does its propagation speed *increase, decrease,* or *remain the same?* Explain.

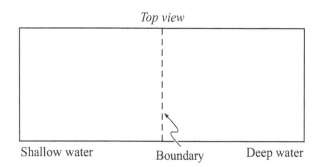

Top view

Shallow water   Boundary   Deep water

B. Suppose that the depth of water on the left side of the boundary is now increased such that the left region is deeper than the right region. The depth on the right is unchanged.

For each region, is the propagation speed after the change *greater than, less than,* or *equal to* its value before the change? Explain.

• left region

• right region

Is it possible to increase the propagation speed of the wave on the right side of the boundary by changing the propagation speed on the left side? Explain.

II. Propagation of a periodic wave

A periodic wave is generated by rocking a dowel back and forth at a steady rate in a large tank of water of uniform depth. The dowel is oriented as shown at right. (Only part of the tank is shown.)

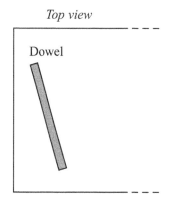

Top view

Dowel

A. On the diagram, (1) sketch several wavefronts (*e.g.,* lines that represent crests of the wave generated by the dowel), and (2) draw an arrow to show the direction of propagation of the wavefronts.

Ask a tutorial instructor to show you a demonstration that you can use to check your answer experimentally.

The direction of propagation of straight wavefronts can be indicated by drawing a ray

(———►——). A diagram in which waves are represented by rays is called a *ray diagram.*

B. On the basis of your observations, describe the orientation of a ray relative to the corresponding wavefronts. Is your answer consistent with the diagram you drew in part A?

III. Water waves passing from shallow water to deep water

A. The diagram at right shows a different tank of water containing two regions of different depths.

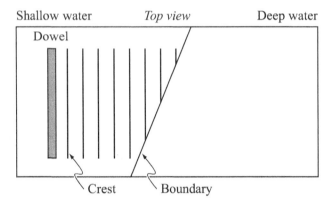

A periodic wave is generated by a dowel in the left region of shallow water. Only the wavefronts in the shallow region are shown.

Make the following predictions based on what you have learned about the behavior of pulses passing from one spring to another.

1. Will a crest be transmitted as *a crest, a trough,* or *something in between?* Explain.

2. Compare the wavelengths and frequencies of the waves in the two regions. Explain.

3. On the diagram above, sketch the wavefronts of the transmitted wave in the region of deep water. (Ignore reflections at the boundary.) Explain.

B. Obtain a photograph that shows wavefronts incident from the left on a boundary between two regions of water and check your answers in part A.

1. Explain how you can tell from the photograph that the region of shallower depth is on the left-hand side of the photograph.

2. Describe how the wavefronts change in crossing the boundary. How can you use your observations in section II to determine the direction of propagation of the transmitted wavefronts?

3. Are your predictions in part A consistent with your answers to the above questions? If not, resolve any inconsistencies.

The conditions that govern the behavior of waves at a boundary between two different media

are typically called *boundary conditions.*

IV. Water waves at a boundary

A. In experiment 1, a periodic wave is generated in a tank of water with two regions of different depth by moving a dowel back and forth with frequency f_o. The wave propagates from deep water into shallow water. It is observed that the propagation speed in the shallow water is *half* that in the deep water. Wavefronts incident on the boundary between the two regions are shown.

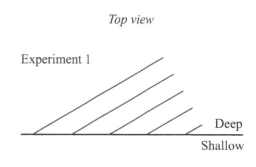

Top view

Experiment 1

Deep

Shallow

Ask a tutorial instructor for an enlargement of the diagram and a set of transparencies.

1. Choose the transparency in which the parallel lines best represent the transmitted wavefronts in experiment 1. Explain.

2. On the enlargement, orient the transparency that you chose to represent the transmitted wavefronts so that the boundary conditions are satisfied.

    Describe the boundary conditions that you used to determine how to orient the transmitted wavefronts.

    Is there more than one possible orientation for the transmitted wavefronts that would satisfy the boundary conditions?

⇨ Check your answers to parts 1 and 2 with a tutorial instructor.

3. On the diagrams below, illustrate a wave passing from deep to shallow water at the angle of incidence shown. On the left diagram, show the wavefronts; on the right one, the rays.

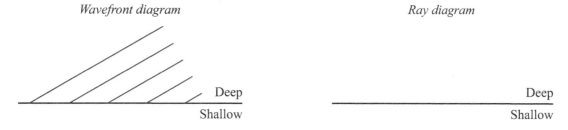

Wavefront diagram

Ray diagram

Deep

Shallow

Deep

Shallow

The change that occurs when a wave propagates into a region of different speed is called *refraction*. The *angle of incidence* is defined as the angle between the ray that represents the incident wave and the *normal* to the boundary. The *angle of refraction* is defined analogously. In the remainder of this tutorial, the subscripts *i* and *r* refer to the *incident* and *refracted* waves respectively.

B. On the ray diagram in part A.3, label the angle of incidence, θ_i, and the angle of refraction, θ_r.

C. In experiment 2, as in experiment 1, a wave is generated by rocking the same dowel back and forth with the same frequency f_o in the same region of deep water. However, some other aspect of the experimental setup has been changed: it is now observed that the propagation speed of the transmitted wave is twice that of the incident wave.

   1. Briefly discuss what change could have been made to the experimental setup used in experiment 1 in order to increase the speed of the transmitted wave.

   2. Choose from your set of transparencies the one in which the parallel lines best represent the transmitted wavefronts in experiment 2. Find an orientation of the incident and transmitted wavefronts so that the boundary conditions are satisfied.

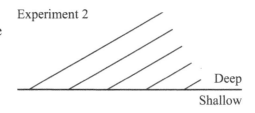

Experiment 2

Deep

Shallow

   • On the diagram above, sketch the transmitted wavefronts in experiment 2.

   • Circle all of the quantities below that are different in experiments 1 and 2.

$$v_i \qquad \lambda_i \qquad f_i \qquad \theta_i \qquad v_r \qquad \lambda_r \qquad f_r \qquad \theta_r$$

   For each of the circled quantities, state whether the quantity in experiment 2 is *larger* or *smaller* than the corresponding quantity in experiment 1. Explain.

Tutorials in Introductory Physics
McDermott, Shaffer, and the P.E.G., U. Wash.

©Pearson
Custom 2nd Ed., for U.CO, Boulder

D. In experiment 3, a wave is generated by rocking a dowel back and forth in region 1. The diagram at right shows both the rays and the corresponding wavefronts of the incident and transmitted waves.

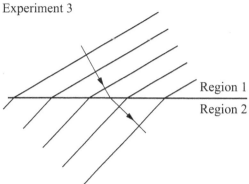

Experiment 3

Region 1
Region 2

1. In experiment 4, a *single* change has been made to experiment 3: the rate at which the dowel is rocked back and forth is twice that in experiment 3.

   • From the choices provided on the last page of the tutorial, choose the diagram that represents the wavefronts in experiment 4. If there is no such diagram, state so explicitly and explain.

   • Circle all of the quantities below that are different in experiments 3 and 4.

   v_i $\quad$ λ_i $\quad$ f_i $\quad$ θ_i $\quad$ v_r $\quad$ λ_r $\quad$ f_r $\quad$ θ_r

   For each of the circled quantities, state whether the quantity in experiment 4 is *larger* or *smaller* than the corresponding quantity in experiment 3. Explain.

2. In experiment 5, a *single* change has been made to experiment 3: the depth of water in region 1 is increased, so that the propagation speed of the incident wave is twice that in experiment 3.

   • From the choices provided on the last page of the tutorial, choose the diagram that represents the wavefronts in experiment 5. If there is no such diagram, state so explicitly and explain.

   • Circle all of the quantities below that are different in experiments 3 and 5.

   v_i $\quad$ λ_i $\quad$ f_i $\quad$ θ_i $\quad$ v_r $\quad$ λ_r $\quad$ f_r $\quad$ θ_r

   For each of the circled quantities, state whether the quantity in experiment 5 is *larger* or *smaller* than the corresponding quantity in experiment 3. Explain.

3. In experiment 6, *two* changes have been made to experiment 3: the rate at which the dowel is moved back and forth is twice that in experiment 3, and the depth of water in region 1 is increased so that the propagation speed of the incident wave is twice that in experiment 3.

    * From the choices provided on the last page of the tutorial, choose the diagram that represents the wavefronts in experiment 6. If there is no such diagram, state so explicitly and explain.

    * Circle all of the quantities below that are different in experiments 3 and 6.

    $$v_i \qquad \lambda_i \qquad f_i \qquad \theta_i \qquad v_r \qquad \lambda_r \qquad f_r \qquad \theta_r$$

    For each of the circled quantities, state whether the quantity in experiment 6 is *larger* or *smaller* than the corresponding quantity in experiment 3. Explain.

Enlarged diagram for experiment 3

Experiment 3

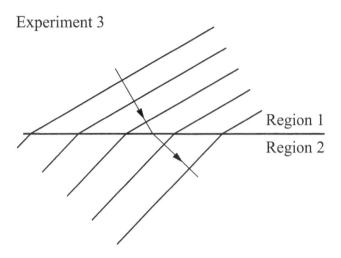

Choices of wavefront diagrams for part D

Diagram A

Diagram B

Diagram C

Diagram D

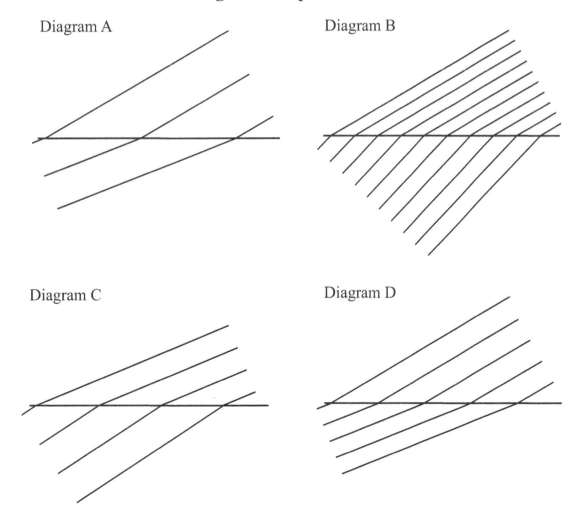

I.   Representations of electromagnetic waves

A.   Shown below are mathematical and pictorial representations of an electromagnetic plane wave propagating through empty space. The electric field is parallel to the z-axis; the magnetic field is parallel to the y-axis. ($\hat{x}$, $\hat{y}$, and $\hat{z}$ are unit vectors along the $+x$-, $+y$-, and $+z$-directions, respectively.)

$$\vec{E}(x, y, z, t) = E_o \sin(kx + \omega t)\, \hat{z} \qquad \vec{B}(x, y, z, t) = B_o \sin(kx + \omega t)\, \hat{y}$$

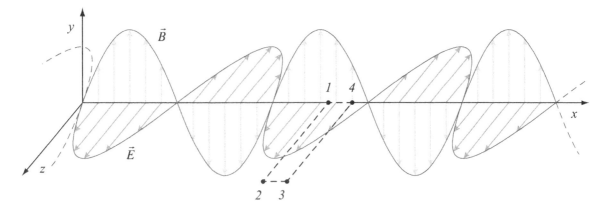

1.   Is the wave transverse or longitudinal? Explain in terms of the quantities that are oscillating.

In which direction is the wave propagating? Justify your answer in two ways:

• using the expressions for the electric field and magnetic field, and

• applying your knowledge of the Poynting vector.

2.   The points $1-4$ in the diagram above lie in the x-z plane.

For the instant shown, rank these points according to the magnitude of the *electric field*. If the electric field is zero at any point, state that explicitly.

Is your ranking consistent with the mathematical expression for the electric field shown above? If not, resolve any inconsistencies. [For example, how, if at all, does changing the value of z affect the value of $\vec{E}(x, y, z, t)$?]

For the instant shown, rank points $1-4$ according to the magnitude of the *magnetic field*. Check that your ranking is consistent with the expression for the magnetic field, $\vec{B}(x, y, z, t)$, above.

3. In the diagram at right, the four points labeled "×" are all located in a plane parallel to the *y-z* plane. One of the labeled points is located on the *x*-axis.

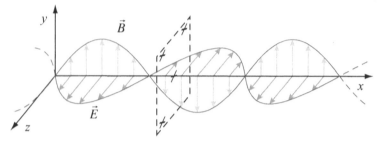

On the diagram, sketch vectors to show the direction and relative magnitude of the electric field at the labeled points.

Justify the use of the term *plane wave* for this electromagnetic wave.

⇨ Check your answers to part A with a tutorial instructor.

B. Three light waves are represented at right. The diagrams are drawn to the same scale.

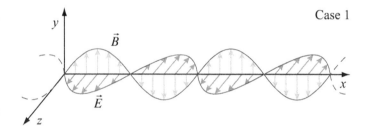

Case 1

1. How is the wave in case 1 different from the wave in case 2? Explain how you can tell from the diagrams.

Case 2

2. If the wave in case 2 were green light, could the wave in case 3 be *red light* or *blue light*? Explain.

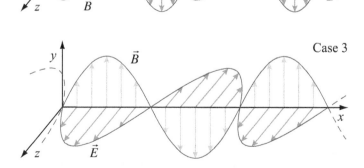

Case 3

Tutorials in Introductory Physics
McDermott, Shaffer, and the P.E.G., U. Wash.

©Pearson
Custom 2nd Ed., for U.CO, Boulder

II. Detecting electromagnetic waves

A.   Write an expression for the force exerted on a charge, q, by (1) an electric field, $\vec{E}$, and (2) a magnetic field, $\vec{B}$.

If an electric field and a magnetic field were both present, would a force be exerted on the charge even if the charge were initially not moving? Explain.

B.   Imagine that the electromagnetic wave in section I is a radio wave. A long, thin conducting wire (see figure at right) is placed in the path of the wave.

Wire

1.   Suppose that the wire were oriented parallel to the z-axis.

As the wave propagates past the wire, would the *electric field* due to the radio wave cause the charges in the wire to move? If so, would the charges move in a direction along the length of the wire? Explain.

As the wave propagates past the wire, would the *magnetic field* due to the wave cause the charges in the wire to move in a direction along the length of the wire? Explain.

2.   Imagine that the thin conducting wire is cut in half and that each half is connected to a different terminal of a light bulb. (See diagram at right.)

Wire

If the wire were placed in the path of the radio wave and oriented parallel to the z-axis, would the bulb ever glow? Explain. (*Hint:* Under what conditions can a bulb glow even if it is not part of a closed circuit?)

Bulb

How, if at all, would your answer change if the wire were oriented:

• parallel to the y-axis? Explain.

• parallel to the x-axis? Explain.

Wire

3.   Suppose that the bulb were disconnected and that each half of the wire were connected in a circuit, as shown. (A conducting wire or rod used in this way is an example of an *antenna*.)

In order to best detect the oncoming radio wave (that is, to maximize the current through the circuit), how should the antenna be oriented relative to the wave? Explain.

Connections
to circuit

III. Supplement: Electromagnetic waves and Maxwell's equations

A. Recall Faraday's law from electricity and magnetism:

$$\oint \vec{E} \cdot \vec{dl} = \frac{-d\Phi_B}{dt}$$

We shall consider how each side of the equation for Faraday's law applies to the imaginary loop, $1 \to 2 \to 3 \to 4 \to 1$, in the figure for part A of section I.

1. For the instant shown in the figure, determine whether each quantity below is *positive, negative,* or *zero.* Explain your reasoning in each case.

   - the quantity $\int \vec{E} \cdot \vec{dl}$ evaluated over the path $1 \to 2$

   - the quantity $\int \vec{E} \cdot \vec{dl}$ evaluated over the path $2 \to 3$

   - the quantity $\oint \vec{E} \cdot \vec{dl}$ evaluated over the entire loop, $1 \to 2 \to 3 \to 4 \to 1$ (*Hint:* The answer is *not* zero.)

   For an imaginary surface that is bounded by a closed loop, it is customary to use the right-hand rule to determine the direction of the area vector that is normal to that surface. For example, the vector that is normal to the flat, imaginary rectangular surface bounded by the loop $1 \to 2 \to 3 \to 4 \to 1$ points in the *positive y*-direction.

2. At the instant shown in the figure, is the magnetic flux through the loop $1 \to 2 \to 3 \to 4 \to 1$ *positive, negative,* or *zero?* Explain how you can tell from the figure.

   A short time later, will the magnetic flux through the loop be *larger, smaller,* or *the same?* Explain how you can tell from the figure.

3. According to your answers in part 2 above, is the quantity $\left(\frac{-d\Phi_B}{dt} \right)$, written on the right-hand side of the equation for Faraday's law, *positive, negative,* or *zero?* Explain.

   According to your results in part 1 above, is the quantity on the left-hand side of this equation *positive, negative,* or *zero?*

   Do you get the same answer for both sides of the equation for Faraday's law? If not, resolve the inconsistencies.

B. Suppose that the electric field in a light wave were $\vec{E}(x, y, z, t) = E_o \sin(kx + \omega t)\, \hat{z}$.

   Would it be possible to have a magnetic field that is *zero* for all x and t? Use Faraday's law to support your answer. (*Hint:* How, if at all, would your answers in part A above be different if the magnetic field were zero for all x and t?)

Tutorials in Introductory Physics
McDermott, Shaffer, and the P.E.G., U. Wash.

©Pearson
Custom 2nd Ed., for U.CO, Boulder

Optics

The activities in this tutorial require a darkened room. *In each experiment, make a prediction before you make any observations.* Resolve any discrepancies before continuing.

I. Light

A. Arrange a very small bulb, a cardboard mask, and a screen as shown at right. Select the largest circular hole (~1 cm in diameter) provided by the mask.

Perspective view

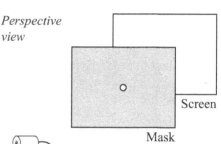

Screen

Mask

Predict what you would see on the screen. Explain in words and with a sketch.

Predict how moving the bulb upward would affect what you see on the screen. Explain.

Perform the experiments and check your predictions. If any of your predictions were incorrect, resolve the inconsistency.

B. *Predict* how each of the following changes would affect what you see on the screen. Explain your reasoning and include sketches that support your predictions.

- The mask is replaced by a mask with a *triangular* hole.

- The bulb is moved farther from the mask.

Perform the experiments and check your predictions. Resolve any inconsistencies.

C. A mask with a circular hole is placed between a bulb and a screen.

Perspective view

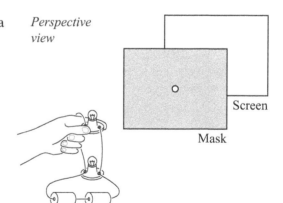

Screen

Mask

Predict how placing a second bulb above the first would affect what you see on the screen. Explain.

Predict how moving the top bulb upward slightly would affect what you see on the screen. Explain.

Perform the experiments. Resolve any inconsistencies.

D. What do your observations suggest about the path taken by light from the bulb to the screen?

Tutorials in Introductory Physics
McDermott, Shaffer, and the P.E.G., U. Wash.

©Pearson
Custom 2nd Ed., for U.CO, Boulder

E. Imagine that you held a string of closely spaced small bulbs one above the other. What would you expect to see on the screen?

Predict what you would see on the screen if you used a bulb with a long filament instead. Explain.

Long-filament bulb

Check your prediction.

F. The mask used in parts C–E is replaced by one that has a triangular hole as shown.

Predict what you would see on the screen when a small bulb is held next to the top of a long-filament bulb as shown. Sketch your prediction below.

Perspective view

Triangular hole

Compare your prediction with those of your partners. After you and your partners have come to an agreement, check your prediction. Resolve any inconsistencies.

G. *Predict* what you would see on the screen in the situation pictured at right.

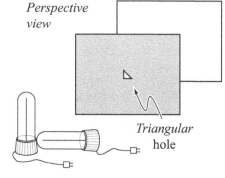

Perspective view

Triangular hole

Predict what you would see on the screen if the mask were *removed*.

Check your predictions. If any of your predictions were incorrect, resolve the inconsistency.

H. *Predict* what you would see on the screen when an ordinary frosted bulb is held in front of a mask with a triangular hole as pictured at right.

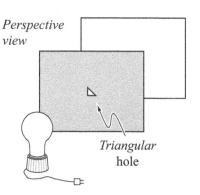

Perspective view

Triangular hole

⇨ Discuss your prediction with a tutorial instructor, then obtain a frosted bulb and check your prediction.

Tutorials in Introductory Physics
McDermott, Shaffer, and the P.E.G., U. Wash.

©Pearson
Custom 2ⁿᵈ Ed., for U.CO, Boulder

II. Light: quantitative predictions

A. *Predict* the size of the lit region on the screen at right. Treat the bulb as a point source of light (*i.e.,* as if all the light emanates from a single point).

Side view
(not to scale)

Circular hole
1 cm in diameter

60 cm

40 cm

Mask

Screen

How would the diameter of the lit region *change* if the diameter of the hole were halved? (In particular, would it become half as big?) Explain.

B. Suppose that the bulb were replaced by a long-filament bulb as shown.

Predict how the height (*i.e.,* vertical dimension) of the lit area would change if the diameter of the hole were halved. (In particular, would it become half as tall?) Explain in words and with a sketch.

Side view
(not to scale)

Circular hole
1 cm in diameter

7.5 cm

60 cm

40 cm

Mask

Screen

Check your prediction. If your prediction was incorrect, resolve the inconsistency.

Predict the *approximate* height and shape of the lit region on the screen in the limit as the hole becomes very small (*e.g.,* the size of a pinhole). (*Hint:* In this limit, would the lit region be *taller than*, *shorter than*, or *the same height as* the filament?)

C. *Predict* what you would see on the screen in the situation pictured at right.

Perspective view

How would the height and width of each lit region *change* if the diameter of the hole in the mask were halved? Explain.

Check your predictions. If any of your predictions were incorrect, resolve the inconsistency.

III. Supplement: Shadows

Obtain a box, thread, and small bead (~5 mm in diameter). Hang the bead as shown.

Perspective view

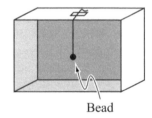

Bead

A. *Predict* what you would see on the screen at the back of the box in the situation pictured at right. Explain your reasoning.

Predict how placing a second bulb above the first would affect what you see on the screen. Explain your reasoning.

Perspective view

Perform the experiments. Resolve any discrepancies between your observations and predictions.

> Must a region be *completely* without light for a shadow to be formed? Explain.

B. Suppose that the light from the top bulb in the situation above were red and the light from the lower bulb were green. Predict what you would see on the screen. Explain.

Obtain red and green filters from a tutorial instructor and perform the experiment described above. If your predictions were incorrect, find the error in your reasoning.

C. *Predict* what you would see on the screen in the situation shown at right. Explain your reasoning.

Perspective view

Suppose that the light from the vertical bulb were red and the light from the horizontal bulb were green. *Predict* what you would see on the screen.

Perform the experiments described above. Resolve any discrepancies between your observations and your predictions.

Tutorials in Introductory Physics
McDermott, Shaffer, and the P.E.G., U. Wash.

©Pearson
Custom 2nd Ed., for U.CO, Boulder

I. The method of parallax

A. Close one eye and lean down so that your open eye is at table level. Have your partner drop a very small piece of paper (about 2 mm square) onto the table.

Hold one finger above the table and then move your finger until you think it is directly above the piece of paper. Move your finger straight down to the table and check whether your finger is, in fact, directly above the paper.

Try this exercise several times, with your partner dropping the piece of paper at different locations. Keep your open eye at table level. After several tries, exchange roles with your partner.

How can you account for the fact that when your finger misses the piece of paper, your finger is always either in front of the paper or behind it, but never to the left or right of the paper?

B. Suppose that you placed your finger behind the paper (as shown at right) while trying to locate the piece of paper.

Predict whether your finger would appear to be located *to the left of, to the right of,* or *in line with* the piece of paper if:

• you moved your head to the left.

• you moved your head to the right.

Top view

Location of your finger

Piece of paper

Your open eye

Check your predictions. Resolve any inconsistencies.

C. Suppose that you had placed your finger in front of the piece of paper rather than behind it.

Predict whether the paper or your finger would appear on the left when you move your head to the left. Check your answer experimentally.

D. Devise a method based on your results from parts B and C by which you could locate the piece of paper. Your method should include how to tell whether your finger is directly over the piece of paper and, if not, whether it is in front of or behind the piece of paper. Describe your method to your partner, then test your method.

⇨ Check your method with a tutorial instructor.

We will refer to the method that you devised for locating the piece of paper as the *method of parallax*.

II. Image location

Obtain a small mirror and two identical nails. Place the mirror in the middle of a sheet of paper. Stand one nail on its head about 10 cm from the front of the mirror. We will call this nail the *object nail*.

Top view

———————— Mirror

On the paper, mark the locations of the mirror and object nail.

●

Object nail

A. Place your head so that you can see the image of the nail in the mirror.

Use the method of parallax to position the second nail so that it is located in the same place as the image of the object nail. Mark this location on the paper.

Is the image of the nail located *on the surface of, in front of,* or *behind* the mirror? Explain.

Would observers at other locations agree that the image is located at the place you marked? Check your answer experimentally.

B. Move the nail off to the right side of the mirror as shown. Find the new image location.

Top view

———————— Mirror

●

Object nail

In the following experiments, we will determine the location of an object and its image by a different technique called *ray tracing*. This technique is based on a model for the behavior of light in which we envision light being either emitted in all directions by a luminous object (such as a light bulb) or reflected in all directions by a non-luminous object (such as a nail).

III. Ray tracing

A. Place a large sheet of paper on the table. Stand a nail vertically at one end of the piece of paper.

Place your eye at table level at the other end of the piece of paper and look at the nail. Use a straightedge to draw a *line of sight* to the nail, that is, a line from your eye to the nail.

Repeat this procedure to mark lines of sight from three other very different vantage points, *then remove the nail.*

How can you use these lines of sight to determine where the nail was located?

What is the smallest number of lines of sight needed to determine the location of the nail? Explain.

B. Turn the large sheet of paper over (or obtain a fresh sheet of paper). Place the mirror in the middle of the sheet of paper, and place a nail in front of the mirror. On the paper, mark the locations of the mirror and the nail.

On the paper, draw several lines of sight to the *image* of the nail.

How can you use these lines of sight to determine the location of the image of the nail?

Use the method of parallax to determine the location of the image of the nail.

Do these two methods yield the same location of the image (to within reasonable uncertainty)?

C. Remove the mirror and the object nail. For each eye location that you used in part B, draw the path that light takes from the object nail to the mirror.

Draw an arrow head on each line segment (———▶———) to indicate the direction that light moves along that part of the path.

On the basis of the paths that you have drawn, formulate a rule that you can use to predict the path that light takes after it is reflected by a mirror.

D. Place the second nail at the location of the image of the object nail. Draw a diagram illustrating the path of the light from that nail to your eye for the same eye locations as in part C.

How is the diagram for this situation similar to the diagram that you drew in part C?

Is there any way that your eye can distinguish between these two situations?

IV. An application of ray tracing

Pin

In this part of the tutorial, use a straightedge and a protractor to draw rays as accurately as possible.

A. On the diagram at right, draw one ray from the pin that is reflected by the mirror.

If you were to place your eye so that you were looking back along the reflected ray, what would you see?

Mirror

From one ray *alone* do you have enough information to determine the location of the image? If not, what can you infer about the location of the image from only a single ray?

B. On the diagram above, draw a second ray from the pin that is reflected by the mirror and that would reach an observer at a different location.

What can you infer about the location of the image from this second ray *alone?*

How can you use the two rays that you have drawn to determine the location of the image?

Is there additional information about the image location that can be deduced from three or more rays?

C. Determine the image location using the method of ray tracing from section III. (If it is necessary to extend a ray to show from where light appears to come, use a *dashed line*.)

Does the light that reaches the observer actually come from the image location or does this light only *appear* to come from that point?

What is the smallest number of rays that you must draw in using ray tracing to determine the location of the image of an object? Explain.

How does the distance between the mirror and the image location compare to the distance between the mirror and the pin?

The diagram that you drew above to determine the image location is called a *ray diagram*. The point from which the reflected light appears to come (*i.e.*, the location of the pin that you saw when you looked in the mirror) is called the *image location*. An image is said to be *virtual* when the light that forms the image does not actually pass through the image location. An image is said to be *real* when the light that forms the image does pass through the image location.

When drawing ray diagrams, use a solid line *with an arrow head* (——▶——) to represent a ray, that is, a path that light takes. Use a dashed line (– – – – – – –) to extend a ray to show from where light *appears* to come in order to distinguish such a line from an actual ray.

I. Cylindrical mirrors

A. A pin is placed in front of a cylindrical mirror as shown in the top view diagram at right. Lines *A–E* represent some of the light rays from the pin that reach the mirror. Points *M* and *N* represent the locations of two observers.

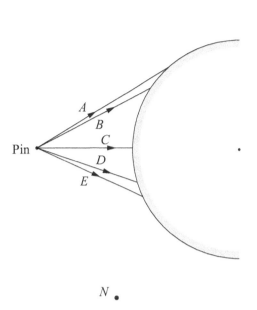

You have been provided with an enlargement of this top view diagram.

1. Use a ruler and a protractor to draw the reflected rays on the enlargement. (*Hint:* The center of the cylindrical mirror is marked on the diagram.)

   Describe how you determined the direction of each reflected ray.

2. For each of the reflected rays, use a dashed line to show the direction from which the reflected ray appears to have come.

   Do all of the reflected rays appear to have come from the same point?

3. On the diagram, draw a ray, *A*′, between rays *A* and *B*. Draw the corresponding reflected ray.

   Which more nearly appear to pass through the same point: the reflected rays *A*, *A*′, and *B* or the reflected rays *A*, *B*, and *C?*

Describe how, in principle, you could determine the location at which an observer at *M* would see an image of the pin. Label the approximate location on the diagram.

Determine and label the approximate location at which an observer at *N* would see an image of the pin.

Would the observers at *M* and *N* agree on the location of the image of the pin? Explain how you can tell from your ray diagram.

4. Ask a tutorial instructor for a semi-cylindrical mirror. Place the mirror on the enlargement and use the method of parallax to check your predictions. (You may find it helpful to tape the mirror onto the diagram.) If there are any inconsistencies between your predictions and your observations, resolve the inconsistencies.

B. Could you use any two rays (even those that do *not* pass near a particular observer) to find the location at which that observer sees the image of the pin in the case of:

  • a plane mirror? Explain.

  • a curved mirror? Explain.

C. Observers at *M* and *N* are looking at an image of the pin in the mirror.

   1. Suppose that all but a small portion of the mirror were covered as shown at right.

      How, if at all, would this change affect what the observers at *M* and *N* see? Explain.

      Determine the region in which an observer must be located in order to see an image of the pin. Discuss your reasoning with your partners.

      Would two observers at different locations in this region agree on the approximate location of the image? Explain.

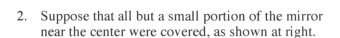

   2. Suppose that all but a small portion of the mirror near the center were covered, as shown at right.

      Determine the region in which an observer must be located in order to see an image of the pin.

      Would two observers at different locations in this region agree on the approximate location of the image? If so, find the approximate image location. If not, explain how you can tell.

Check your answers experimentally.

While the image location is independent of observer location in certain cases (*e.g.,* plane mirrors), in general it is not. In many cases, however, it is possible to identify a limited range of locations for which the image location is essentially independent of the observer location. An example is when both the object and the observer lie very nearly along the axis of a cylindrical or spherical mirror. In this situation, all rays are said to be *paraxial,* that is, they make small angles with the axis of the mirror. Ray diagrams often specify the location of an image but not the observer's location. For such a diagram, it should be assumed that the image location is independent of the observer's location.

II. Multiple plane mirrors

A. Stick a pin into a piece of cardboard and place two mirrors at right angles near the pin as shown in the top view diagram below.

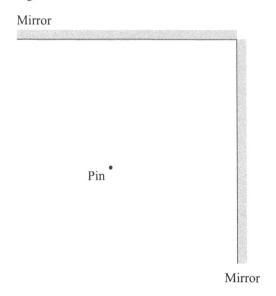

Mirror

Pin

Mirror

1. Describe what you observe.

2. View the arrangement from several locations and use the method of parallax to place a pin at each of the image locations.

3. Suppose that one of the mirrors were removed. Predict which image(s) you would still see and which image(s) would vanish.

    Check your predictions. If any of your predictions were incorrect, resolve the conflict before continuing.

4. On the diagram above, sketch a ray diagram that accounts for each image.

    Describe how one of the images differs from the others.

B. Gradually decrease the angle between the mirrors while keeping the pin between the mirrors.

How can you account for the presence of the additional images that you observe?

I. Image location

A. A pin is held vertically at the back of a clear square container of water as shown at right. The portion of the pin below the surface of the water is not shown.

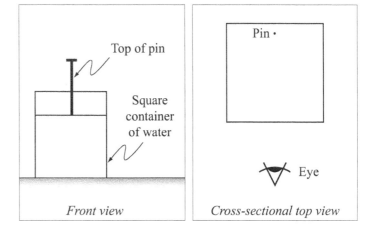

Top of pin

Square container of water

Front view

Pin ·

Eye

Cross-sectional top view

1. On an enlargement of the top view diagram, sketch several rays from the pin that pass through the water and out the front of the container, near the observer's eye.

For simplicity in answering the following questions, ignore the walls of the container (*i.e.*, use the approximation that light passes directly from water to air, where it travels more quickly).

• On the basis of the rays that you have drawn, *predict* where the bottom of the pin would *appear* to be located to the observer. Discuss your reasoning with your partners.

• Would the bottom of the pin *appear* to be located *closer to, farther from,* or *the same distance from* the observer as the top of the pin? Explain.

2. Obtain the necessary equipment and use the method of parallax to check your predictions. If your ray diagram is not consistent with your observations, modify your ray diagram.

The place where the pin *appears* to be located is called the location of the image of the pin, or the *image location*.

3. In part 1, you assumed that light from the pin passes directly from water to air. Devise an experiment that would allow you to test whether this approximation is valid. (*Hint:* Use the method of parallax to see how the container *alone* affects the apparent location of the pin.)

Perform this experiment and check your answer.

Tutorials in Introductory Physics
McDermott, Shaffer, and the P.E.G., U. Wash.

©Pearson
Custom 2nd Ed., for U.CO, Boulder

B. Suppose that a pencil were held vertically at the back of a circular beaker of water, as shown. (The portion of the pencil below the surface of the water is not shown.) *Note:* The center of the beaker is marked by an "×."

Is the image of the bottom of the pencil *closer to, farther from,* or *the same distance from* the observer as the top of the pencil?

Sketch a qualitatively correct ray diagram to support your answer.

Front view

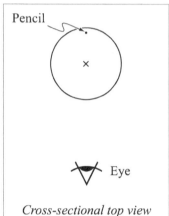

Cross-sectional top view

Use the method of parallax to place a second pencil at the location of the image of the bottom of the pencil, and check your predictions. If your prediction was incorrect, find your error.

C. Three students are discussing their results from part B:

Student 1: "I think that the image is closer to me than the pencil itself. The closer something is, the bigger it looks. Because the image of the pencil appears wider than the pencil itself, the image must be closer to me than the pencil."

Student 2: "That sounds reasonable, but when I used parallax to determine the location of the image of the pencil, I found that it was farther from me than the pencil."

Student 3: "That doesn't make sense though. If the image were behind the pencil, then how could I see the image? Wouldn't the pencil block my view of the image?"

Do you agree or disagree with each of these students? Discuss your reasoning with your partners.

Tutorials in Introductory Physics
McDermott, Shaffer, and the P.E.G., U. Wash.

©Pearson
Custom 2ⁿᵈ Ed., for U.CO, Boulder

II. Real and virtual images

Each of the ray diagrams below illustrates the path of light from a pin through a beaker of water. In one case, the pin is near the beaker of water; in the other case, far from the beaker.

A. For each case shown below, determine and label the location of the image of the pin. Explain how you determined your answer.

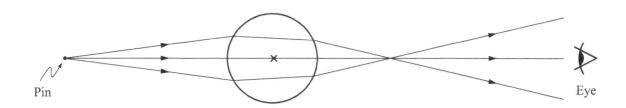

1. Use the ray diagrams above to answer the following questions:

    In each case, which is farther from the observer:

    • the image (below the water's surface) or
    • the object (above the water's surface)?

    In each case, which is farther from the observer:

    • the image (below the water's surface) or
    • the beaker of water?

2. Use the method of parallax to check your answers for both cases 1 and 2. Resolve any inconsistencies.

B. In each of the previous cases, predict what would be seen on a white paper screen placed at the image location. Imagine that the room has been darkened but that the pin is illuminated. (*Hint:* In either case, does the light from the pin that forms the image pass through the image location?)

Replace the pin with a lighted long-filament bulb and check your predictions. If either of your predictions were incorrect, resolve the inconsistency.

C. One of the images in part A is real; the other, virtual. Explain how you can tell which image is real and which is virtual on the basis of (1) the ray diagrams and (2) your observations in part B.

D. Explain how you can use a screen to determine the location of an image. In what cases, if any, would this method fail?

In this tutorial, use a straightedge to draw lines that are meant to be straight.

I. Convex lenses

A. Look at a very distant object through a convex lens. Hold the lens at arm's length so that you see a sharp image of the distant object.

Is the image formed by the lens *in front of, behind,* or *on the surface of* the lens? Use the method of parallax to determine the approximate distance between the image and the lens.

B. Consider a point on the distant object that is also on the principal axis of the lens.

On the diagram below, sketch several rays from this distant point that reach the lens.

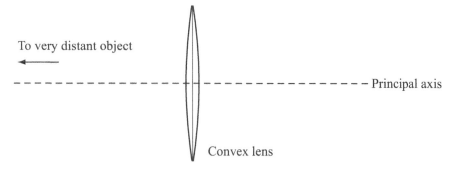

How are these rays oriented with respect to one another and to the principal axis? Explain.

On the basis of your observations from part A, show the continuation of each of these rays through the lens and out the other side. On the diagram, indicate where the rays converge.

Note: Refraction takes place at the two surfaces of the lens. However, in drawing a ray diagram for a thin lens, it is customary to draw rays as if all refraction takes place at the center of the lens.

C. Suppose that you placed a very small bulb at the location of the image in part B.

How would the rays from the bulb that have passed through the lens be oriented? Draw a diagram to illustrate your answer. Explain.

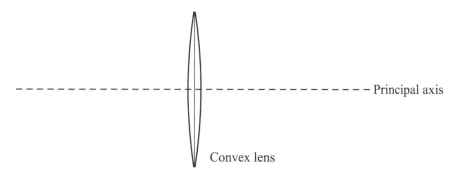

⇨ Discuss your answers with a tutorial instructor.

Tutorials in Introductory Physics
McDermott, Shaffer, and the P.E.G., U. Wash.

©Pearson
Custom 2nd Ed., for U.CO, Boulder

The point of intersection of the principal axis and the image of a very distant object is called the *focal point*. The distance between the center of the lens and the focal point is called the *focal length*.

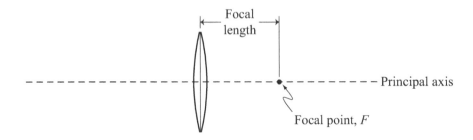

II. Ray tracing and convex lenses

The diagram below shows several rays from the eraser on a pencil that reach a convex lens.

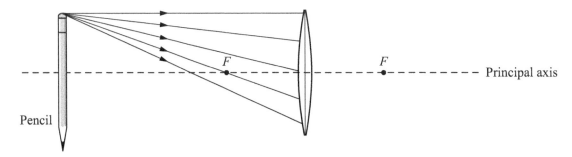

A. Consider the ray that is parallel to the principal axis.

Explain how you can use your observations from section I to draw the continuation of that ray on the right side of the lens. Draw this ray on the diagram.

B. Consider the ray that goes through the focal point on the left side of the lens.

Explain how you can use your answers to part C of section I to draw the continuation of that ray on the right side of the lens. Draw this ray on the diagram.

C. How can you use these two rays to determine the location of the image of the eraser? On the diagram, label the image location.

Tutorials in Introductory Physics
McDermott, Shaffer, and the P.E.G., U. Wash.

©Pearson
Custom 2nd Ed., for U.CO, Boulder

D. Consider the ray from the eraser that strikes the lens near its center, where the sides of the lens are nearly parallel.

Using the image location as a guide, draw the continuation of this ray through the lens and out the other side.

In your own words, describe the path of a ray that passes through the center of the lens.

E. Draw the continuation of the two remaining rays shown on the diagram through the lens and out the other side.

The rays that you drew in parts A, B, and D are called *principal rays*, and they are useful in determining the location of an image. In some cases, one or more of these rays may not actually pass through the lens; however, they may still be used in determining the image location. The principal rays are only a few of the infinitely many that we might draw from one point on the object.

F. On the diagram on the previous page, use the three principal rays from the *tip* of the pencil to determine the location of the image of the tip of the pencil. If possible, use a different color ink or pencil for this second set of rays.

G. The diagram below shows a small object placed near a convex lens. Draw all three principal rays and determine the location of the image. Clearly label the image location.

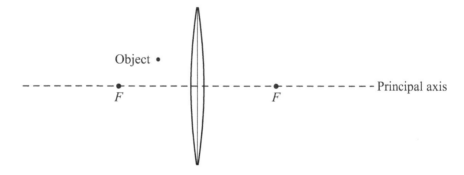

In your own words, describe how you knew to draw each ray.

III. Applications

A. A lens, a bulb, and a screen are arranged as shown below. A sharp, inverted image of the filament (not shown) appears on the screen when it is at the location shown.

Bulb

Lens

Screen

Predict how each of the following changes would affect what you see on the screen. Support your predictions with one or more ray diagrams.

- The screen is moved *closer to* or *farther from* the lens.

- The top half of the lens is covered by a mask.

  Does your answer depend on which side of the lens the mask is placed? If so, how? If not, why not?

B. Obtain the necessary equipment and check your predictions. In the space below, record how, if at all, your predictions were different from your observations. If your predictions were incorrect, resolve the inconsistencies.

C. If the screen were removed, would you still be able to see an image of the bulb? Does it matter where your eye is located?

Turn off (but do not move) the bulb, remove the screen, and check your predictions. If your predictions were incorrect, resolve the inconsistencies. (*Hint:* Was a screen necessary to see an image in earlier situations, such as the situation in part A of section I?)

Tutorials in Introductory Physics
McDermott, Shaffer, and the P.E.G., U. Wash.

©Pearson
Custom 2nd Ed., for U.CO, Boulder

I. Apparent size

A. The diagram at right illustrates what an observer sees when looking at two boxes on a large table.

From the diagram *alone:*

- is it possible to determine which box is closer to the observer?

- is it possible to determine which box *appears* wider to the observer?

- is it possible to determine which box *actually is* wider?

Discuss your reasoning with your partners.

B. Obtain two soda cans and a cardboard tube that has a smaller diameter than the can.

1. How can you arrange the two soda cans so that (a) they *appear* to be equally wide and (b) one can *appears* wider than the other?

   In the space below, draw a top view diagram for each case that can be used to compare the apparent widths of the cans.

2. How can you arrange one can and the tube so that (a) the two objects *appear* to be equally wide and (b) the tube *appears* wider than the can?

   In the space below, draw a top view diagram for each case that can be used to compare the apparent widths of the two objects.

3. What quantities affect the apparent size of an object? Describe how increasing or decreasing each quantity affects the apparent size of that object.

   Explain how you can use a top view diagram to determine whether one object *appears* wider or narrower than another object to an observer at a particular location.

Tutorials in Introductory Physics
McDermott, Shaffer, and the P.E.G., U. Wash.

©Pearson
Custom 2nd Ed., for U.CO, Boulder

II. The image of an extended object

The ray diagram below shows a side view of a thin converging lens, a pencil, the image of the pencil, and five observer locations *(1–5)*. Two rays from the pencil tip are drawn through the lens.

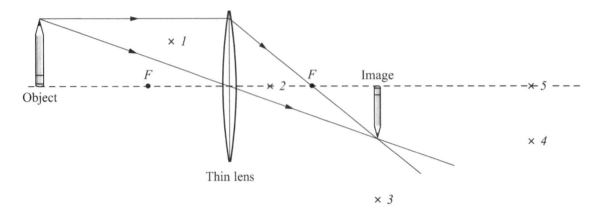

A. Could an observer at each of the labeled points see a sharp image of the pencil tip (other than the actual pencil tip)? In each case, explain why or why not. Additionally, if an observer is able to see the image, indicate the direction that the observer would have to look to see the image.

  • point *1*

  • point *2*

  • point *3*

  • point *4*

  • point *5*

B. Use the above diagram to answer the following questions.

  1. From which of the labeled points could an observer see the image of the *eraser?* Draw rays to support your answer. (If possible, use a different color ink to draw these rays.)

    From which point(s) could an observer see the entire image of the pencil? Explain.

    To an observer at such a point, which would *appear* larger: the image of the pencil (with the lens in place) or the pencil (with the lens removed)? Explain how you can tell from the ray diagram.

2. If you were to measure the length of the pencil and the length of the image using a ruler, which would actually be larger? Explain how you can tell from the ray diagram.

⇨ Check your results for section II with a tutorial instructor.

III. A magnifying glass

A. Obtain a convex lens. Use the lens as a *magnifying glass*, that is, to make an object such as a pencil appear larger. Start with the lens very close to the object.

Which is farther from you: the image or the object?

Where is the *object* relative to the lens and its focal points? (For example, is the object distance *greater than*, *less than*, or *equal to* the focal length of the lens?)

B. Draw a ray diagram that shows how to determine the location of the image that you observed above. Your diagram need not be drawn exactly to scale, but should correctly show the location of the object relative to the observer and to the lens and its focal points.

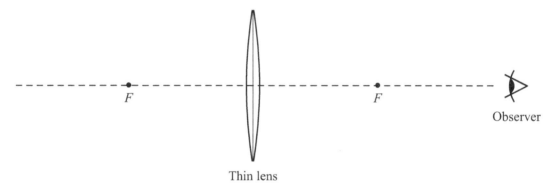

Thin lens

1. On the basis of your ray diagram, which is farther from the observer: the image or the object?

Is your answer consistent with your observations from part A? If not, resolve the inconsistency.

2. Does a magnifying glass simply make an object *appear* closer (*i.e.*, does it simply form an image of the object that is closer to you than the object itself)? If not, what does it do?

3. How can you tell from your ray diagram which would appear larger: the image of the pencil (with the lens in place) or the pencil (with the lens removed)?

IV. Magnification

A. The *lateral magnification, m_L,* is defined as $m_L = h'/h$, where h' and h represent the heights of the image and object, respectively. By convention, h' and h have opposite signs when the image is inverted.

Does the value of the lateral magnification depend on the location of the observer? Explain.

Consider the two examples in this tutorial. In each case, is the absolute value of the lateral magnification *greater than, less than,* or *equal to* one? (If your answer depends on observer location, choose an observer who can see the entire image.)

Does the lateral magnification tell you whether the image will *appear* larger than the object without the lens? Explain why or why not.

B. The *angular magnification, m_θ,* is defined as $m_\theta = \theta'/\theta$, where θ' and θ represent the angular sizes of the image and object, respectively. By convention, θ' and θ have opposite signs when the image is inverted.

Does the value of the angular magnification depend on the location of the observer? Explain.

Consider the two examples in this tutorial. In each case, is the *absolute value* of the angular magnification *greater than, less than,* or *equal to* one? (If your answer depends on observer location, choose an observer who can see the entire image.)

Does the angular magnification tell you whether the image will *appear* larger than the object without the lens? Explain why or why not.

⇨ Check your answers for section IV with a tutorial instructor.

I. Periodic circular waves

The diagram at right shows the wavefronts of a periodic circular wave in a portion of a large ripple tank. Dark circles represent crests and dashed circles represent troughs. The diagram, like a photograph, shows the wavefronts at one instant in time.

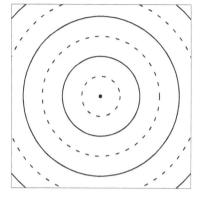

How, if at all, would the diagram differ:

• one-quarter period later? Explain.

• one period later? Explain.

II. Periodic circular waves: Two sources a fixed distance apart

A. The diagram at right illustrates the wavefronts due to each of two small sources.

How do the frequencies of the two sources compare? Explain how you can tell.

Are the two sources in phase or out of phase with respect to each other? Explain how you can tell.

What is the source separation? Express your answer in terms of the wavelength.

Tutorials in Introductory Physics
McDermott, Shaffer, and the P.E.G., U. Wash.

©Pearson
Custom 2nd Ed., for U.CO, Boulder

B. Describe what happens at a point on the surface of the water where:

   • a crest meets a crest

   • a trough meets a trough

   • a crest meets a trough

   For each of the above cases, describe how your answer would differ if the amplitudes of the two waves were *not* equal. Explain your reasoning.

If the waves from two identical sources travel different distances to reach a particular point, the amplitudes of the waves from the two sources will not be the same at that point. For points that are sufficiently far from the sources, however, this difference in the amplitudes of the waves is small. For the remainder of this tutorial, we will *ignore* any such variations in amplitude.

C. Obtain a larger version of the diagram of the wavefronts due to two sources.

   Use different symbols (or different colors) to mark the places at which *for the instant shown:*

   • the displacement of the water surface is zero (*i.e.,* at its equilibrium level)
   • the displacement of the water surface is the greatest above equilibrium
   • the displacement of the water surface is the greatest below equilibrium

   What patterns do you notice? Sketch the patterns on the diagram in part A.

D. The representation that we have been using indicates the shape of the water surface at one particular instant in time.

   Consider a point on your diagram where a crest meets a crest.

   How would the displacement of the water surface at this point change over time? (For example, what would the displacement be one-quarter period later? What would it be one-half period later?)

   Consider what happens at a point on your diagram where a crest meets a trough.

   How will the displacement of the water surface at this point change over time?

E. Suppose that a small piece of paper were floating on the surface of the water. On the basis of your diagram, predict where the paper would move (1) the least and (2) the most.

F. Consider a point where the water surface remains undisturbed.

Explain why that point *cannot* be the same distance from the two sources that we are considering.

For the two sources that we are considering, by how much must the distances from that point to the two sources differ?

Is there more than one possible value for the difference in distances? If so, list the other possible value(s). Explain.

G. Choose a variety of points where the water surface remains undisturbed.

For each of these points, determine the difference in distances from the two sources to the point. (We will represent this difference in distances by ΔD. It is also called *the path length difference*.)

Divide all of the points where the water surface remains undisturbed into groups that have the same value of ΔD. Label each group with the appropriate value of ΔD in terms of the wavelength λ.

Justify the term *nodal lines* for groups of points that are far from the sources.

H. Group the points where there is maximum constructive interference according to their value of ΔD. We will call these *lines of maximum constructive interference*.

Label each group with the appropriate value of ΔD, in terms of the wavelength, λ.

I. Label each of the nodal lines and lines of maximum constructive interference with the corresponding value of $\Delta \varphi$, the phase difference between the waves from the two sources.

J. Imagine observing the waves from above the ripple tank. How, if at all, would the nodal lines and lines of maximum constructive interference change over time? Explain.

What patterns and symmetries do you notice in the arrangement of the nodal lines and the lines of maximum constructive interference?

⇨ Check your answers above with a tutorial instructor.

As you saw above, different points in a ripple tank with two sources that are in phase can have different values of ΔD. At a point for which $\Delta D = 3\lambda/2$, the phase difference between the waves is $\Delta \varphi = 3\pi$ (or 540°) or, more simply, π (or 180°). It is generally acceptable to specify phase differences to be between 0 and 2π (or between 0° and 360°). In this way, the phase difference between the waves at *any* point on *any* nodal line is π (or 180°) and the phase difference between the waves at *any* point of maximum constructive interference is 0 (or 0°).

III. Periodic circular waves: Effect of changing the source separation and frequency

A. Obtain a piece of paper and a transparency with concentric circles on them. The circles represent wavefronts generated by each of two point sources.

Suppose that the two sources are in phase and at the same location. Overlay the transparency on the paper to model this situation.

Explain why there are *no* nodal lines in this case.

Gradually increase the source separation until you first see nodal lines.

What is the source separation when this occurs? In the space at right, sketch the nodal lines and the lines of maximum constructive interference for this situation.

Why can there be no nodal lines for a smaller source separation? Explain. *(Hint:* For a given source separation, what is the largest possible value of $\Delta D?)*

Continue to increase the source separation and investigate how the source separation affects the number of nodal lines and their locations.

B. The diagram at right illustrates the wavefronts due to
two small sources tapping the water surface with
frequency f_o. The sources are separated by a
distance d.

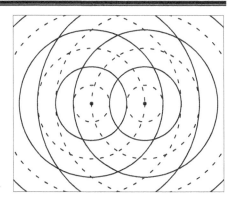

Suppose that the frequency of the two sources were
decreased ($f < f_o$) while the distance between the
sources remains unchanged.

1. Choose one or more cases below that illustrate the
wavefronts due to the two sources after the
frequency has been decreased. (Larger versions of
these diagrams have been provided.)

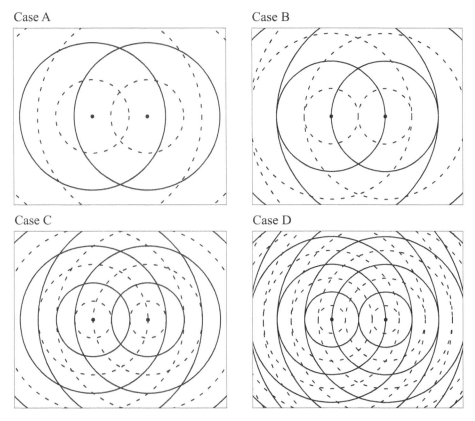

Case A

Case B

Case C

Case D

2. For each case that you selected, determine the source separation d in terms of the
wavelength λ.

3. Describe how a decrease in the frequency affects the number of nodal lines and their
locations.

C. Compare and contrast how changing (1) the source separation, d, and (2) the frequency, f,
affect the number of nodal lines and their locations. Explain.

I. Water waves incident on a single slit

A. Obtain a pan of water and form a barrier in it that has a wide slit as shown. Place a dowel in the water and gently rock it back and forth to generate straight wavefronts at a constant rate.

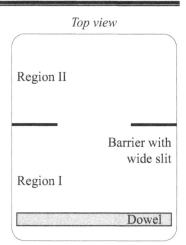

Top view

Region II

Barrier with wide slit

Region I

Dowel

Gradually decrease the width of the slit until it is completely closed. Observe the wavefronts in region II as you make this change.

   1. Describe how the shape of the wavefronts in region II is affected as the width of the slit is decreased.

   2. Compare the spacing of the wavefronts in the two regions (I and II). Is the spacing of the wavefronts in region II affected by changing the width of the slit?

      Explain how your observation of the spacing of the wavefronts is consistent with the relative wave speeds in the two regions.

   3. How, if at all, does the amplitude of the wave in region II change when the slit is made slightly narrower? In particular, consider two cases in which:

      • the slit is initially very wide and is made slightly narrower.

      • the slit is initially very narrow and is made even narrower.

B. It is difficult to make periodic waves using the equipment at your table. Ask a tutorial instructor for photographs of periodic waves incident on slits of various widths.

   1. Are the wavefronts in the photographs consistent with your observations above?

   2. Identify the picture(s) in which the slit acts most like a point source of water waves. Explain.

      How could you modify the situation in this photograph in order to make the slit act more like a point source of waves?

   3. Identify the photograph(s) in which the slit does not significantly affect the shape of the wavefronts.

      How could you modify the situation in this photograph so that the slit affects the wavefronts that pass through the slit to an even lesser extent?

Tutorials in Introductory Physics
McDermott, Shaffer, and the P.E.G., U. Wash.

©Pearson
Custom 2nd Ed., for U.CO, Boulder

As you have observed, the behavior of waves passing through a slit can depend on the size of the slit. For the remainder of this tutorial, we will consider the case of waves passing through two very narrow slits.

II. Water waves incident on two very narrow slits

For this part of the tutorial, you will not be asked to perform any experiments.

A. A periodic water wave is incident on a barrier with two identical narrow slits. Each slit is narrow enough so that it may be treated as a (single) source of circular wavefronts.

   Describe the shape of the wavefronts that emanate from each slit.

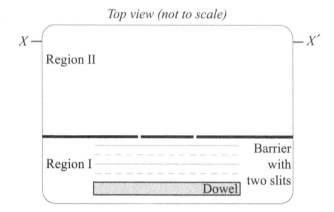

B. Obtain an enlargement of the diagram at right that shows the wavefronts for the case in which the distance between the centers of the slits is 3λ.

   For this situation, which values of ΔD (the difference in distances from a point to each of the slits) correspond to (1) nodal lines and (2) lines of maximum constructive interference? Explain.

   At how many points along the line X–X' in the diagram above is there (1) complete destructive interference and (2) maximum constructive interference? Mark the *approximate* locations of all of these points on the diagram above, and label each point with the corresponding value of ΔD. Assume that the tank is very wide and that the line X–X' is very far from the slits.

C. Suppose that the width of *one* of the slits were decreased (without changing the distance between the centers of the slits). How, if at all, would this modification affect how much the water surface would move at the points you marked above? Explain your reasoning. (*Hint:* How can you use your observations from part A of section I in this case?)

   Thus far we have observed the behavior of *water waves* when they pass through narrow slits.

   Below we investigate the behavior of *light* passing through two very narrow slits.

III. Light incident on two narrow slits

A. Red light from a distant point source is incident on a mask with two identical, narrow vertical slits. The photograph at right illustrates the pattern that appears at the center of a distant screen.

Pattern on screen

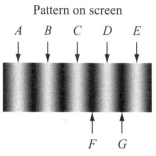

How is this pattern *different* from what you would predict using the ideas developed in geometrical optics (*e.g.*, light travels in straight lines through slits)?

B. Compare the situation in section II (in which a periodic water wave was incident on two identical, narrow slits) to the experiment described above.

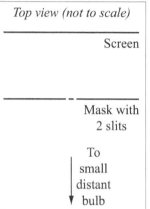

Which points along line *X–X'* in the ripple tank best correspond to:

• points of minimum intensity *(e.g., points F and G)?* Explain.

• points of maximum intensity *(e.g., points A–E)?* Explain.

For a point of minimum intensity *(e.g., points F and G)*, identify the quantity or quantities that add to zero at that point. Explain your reasoning.

C. For each of the lettered points, determine Δ*D* (in terms of λ) and Δ*φ*, the phase difference between the waves. Record your answers below. *Note:* Point *C* is at the center of the screen.

	point *A*	point *B*	point *C*	point *D*	point *E*	point *F*	point *G*
Δ*D*							
Δ*φ*							

D. Suppose that one of the slits were covered.

At which, if any, of the points *A–G* would the brightness increase? Explain.

At which, if any, of the points *A–G* would the brightness decrease? Explain.

In the space at right, sketch the pattern that would appear on the portion of screen shown in the above photograph when one of the slits is covered. Explain.

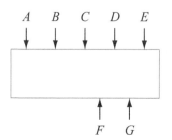

E. The pattern produced by red light passing through two very narrow slits has been reproduced at right.

In each part below, suppose that a *single* change were made to the original apparatus. For each case, determine how, if at all, that change would affect the pattern on the screen. Sketch your predictions in the spaces provided.

Pattern on screen

Center of screen

1. the distance between the slits is decreased (without changing the width of the slits)

2. the screen is moved closer to the mask containing the slits

3. the wavelength of the incident light is decreased

4. the width of each slit is decreased (without changing the distance between the slits)

F. Consider point *B*, the first maximum to the left of the center of the screen.

Pattern on screen

B   C

Suppose that the two slits are separated by 0.2 mm, that the screen is 1.2 m away from the slits, and that the distance from the center of the pattern (point *C*) to point *B* is 3.6 mm.

Use this information to determine the wavelength of the light. Describe any approximations that you make in answering this question.

Top view (not to scale)

Screen

Mask with
2 slits

To
small
distant
bulb

Tutorials in Introductory Physics
McDermott, Shaffer, and the P.E.G., U. Wash.

©Pearson
Custom 2nd Ed., for U.CO, Boulder

I. Double-slit interference

A. Red light from a distant point source is incident on two very narrow identical slits, S_1 and S_2, separated by a distance d. The photograph at right illustrates the pattern that appears on a distant screen.

The magnified view shows the path from slit S_1 to point X, a point on the screen.

On the magnified view:

- Draw an arrow to show the direction from slit S_2 to point X.

- Identify and label the line segment of length ΔD that represents how much farther light travels from one slit than from the other to reach point X.

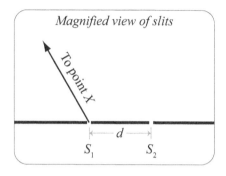

Magnified view of slits

B. In a previous homework, you found an expression for ΔD in terms of d and θ that was valid for points far from two point sources. Using that expression, write equations (in terms of λ, θ, and d) that you can use to calculate the angle(s) for which there will be:

- maximum constructive interference (*i.e.*, a *maximum*)

- complete destructive interference (*i.e.*, a *minimum*)

C. Suppose that the screen were semicircular, as shown.

On the diagram, mark the locations of *all* minima and maxima for the specific case $d = 2.4\lambda$.

Label each maximum and minimum with the corresponding value of:

- ΔD,

- θ, and

- $\Delta\varphi$, the phase difference between the waves from the two slits.

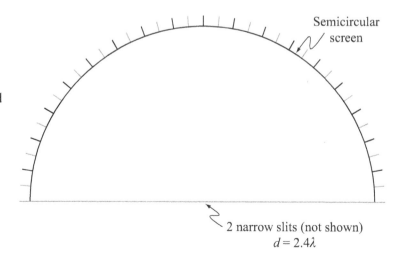

Semicircular screen

2 narrow slits (not shown)
$d = 2.4\lambda$

Tutorials in Introductory Physics
McDermott, Shaffer, and the P.E.G., U. Wash.

©Pearson
Custom 2nd Ed., for U.CO, Boulder

II. Three-slit interference

A. Consider a point *M* on the distant screen where there is a *maximum* due to the light from S_1 and S_2.

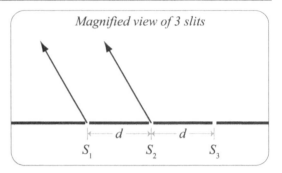

Magnified view of 3 slits

If a third slit were added as shown at right, would there *still* be maximum constructive interference at point *M*? Explain.

Suppose that more identical slits were added with all adjacent slits a distance *d* apart.

Would there still be maximum constructive interference at point *M*? Explain.

For two slits, you found that any point of maximum constructive interference is farther from one of the slits by a whole number of wavelengths (*i.e.*, ΔD is 0, λ, 2λ,...).

For three or more evenly-spaced slits, what is the corresponding condition for locations of maximum constructive interference? Write an expression for ΔD_{adj} in terms of λ that expresses this condition, where ΔD_{adj} is the difference in distances from two *adjacent* slits to a location on the screen.

We will call a location at which light from *all* of the slits is in phase a *principal maximum.*

B. Consider a point *N* on the screen where there is a *minimum* due to the light from S_1 and S_2.

Will the screen remain completely dark at point *N* after the third slit is added as shown above? If not, will point *N* be as bright as a principal maximum? Explain.

Tutorials in Introductory Physics
McDermott, Shaffer, and the P.E.G., U. Wash.

©Pearson
Custom 2nd Ed., for U.CO, Boulder

C. Obtain a set of transparencies of sinusoidal curves. Each transparency can represent the light from a single narrow slit. In particular, what quantity or quantities can these curves be used to represent?

Find a way to align three sinusoidal curves so they would add in a way that results in a minimum for three slits.

What is the smallest value of ΔD_{adj} that corresponds to a minimum for three slits?

Would twice this value also correspond to a minimum? three times? four times?

Write out the first few values of ΔD_{adj} that correspond to minima for three slits. Write out enough values to clearly indicate the pattern.

How many minima are there between adjacent principal maxima for three slits?

D. On the diagram at right, mark the locations of *all* minima and principal maxima for the specific case of three identical slits separated by a distance $d = 2.4\lambda$.

Label each minimum and principal maximum with the corresponding value of:

• ΔD_{adj},

• θ, and

• $\Delta\varphi_{adj}$, the phase difference between the waves from *adjacent* slits.

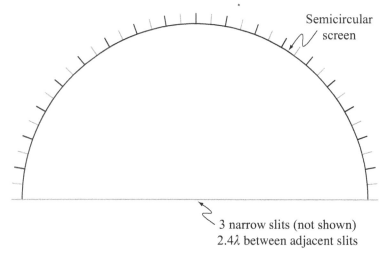

Semicircular screen

3 narrow slits (not shown)
2.4λ between adjacent slits

Compare and contrast this sketch with your sketch from part C of section I for the case of light incident on two slits separated by $d = 2.4\lambda$. Discuss the similarities and differences.

III. Multiple-slit interference

A. Suppose that coherent red light were incident on a mask with four narrow slits a distance d apart.

Use the transparencies of sinusoidal curves to find the smallest value of ΔD_{adj} that would correspond to a minimum for this case.

Which integer multiples of this value of ΔD_{adj} would correspond to other minima? Which would not?

Which values of ΔD_{adj} would correspond to the principal maxima?

How many minima would there be between adjacent principal maxima?

B. Generalize your results from the 2-slit, 3-slit, and 4-slit cases to determine the smallest value of ΔD_{adj} that would correspond to a minimum for the case of N identical, evenly-spaced slits.

Which integer multiples of this value of ΔD_{adj} would correspond to other minima? Which would not?

How many minima would there be between adjacent principal maxima?

C. Coherent red light is incident on a mask with two very narrow slits a distance d apart. The photograph at right illustrates the pattern that appears on a distant screen.

On the photograph, label each of the maxima and minima with the corresponding value of ΔD_{adj}.

Suppose that a *third* slit were added to the mask so that adjacent slits were separated by the same distance d as before.

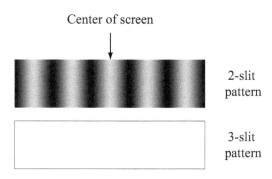

Center of screen

2-slit pattern

3-slit pattern

In the space provided above, sketch the pattern that you would expect to see on the same part of the screen. On your sketch, clearly label each minimum and principal maximum with the corresponding value of ΔD_{adj}.

Ask a tutorial instructor for photographs that illustrate the patterns that appear on a distant screen when light is incident on two masks: one with two slits and one with three slits.

D. How would the pattern differ if the mask contained *four* slits separated by the same distance *d* as before? Sketch your prediction in the space provided at right. Explain your reasoning.

Center of screen

2-slit pattern

4-slit pattern

How would the pattern differ if the mask contained *five* slits separated by the same distance *d* as before? Explain your reasoning.

Ask a tutorial instructor for photographs that illustrate the patterns that appear on a distant screen when light is incident on masks with different numbers of slits.

I. Determining the location of the first minimum for many slits

A. Red light from a distant point source is incident on a mask with ten identical, evenly-spaced, very narrow slits. (See diagrams at right and below.)

On the magnified view below, label the line segment of length ΔD_{adj} that represents how much farther light must travel from slit 1 than from slit 2 to reach point X on a distant screen.

What is the *smallest* value of ΔD_{adj} that corresponds to a minimum for 10 slits? (Transparencies of sine curves are available in case you would like to review these concepts.)

The minimum that corresponds to this smallest value of ΔD_{adj}

is called the *first minimum*.

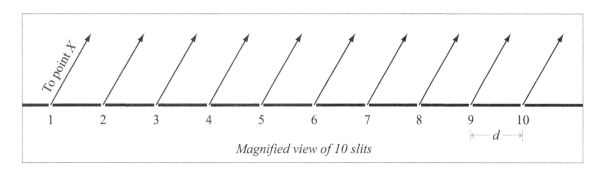

Magnified view of 10 slits

B. Suppose that point X marks the location of the first minimum on the screen.

How much farther (in terms of λ) does the light from slit 1 travel than the light from slit 3 in reaching point X? Explain.

C. Suppose that only slit 1 is uncovered, and all other slits 2–10 are covered. Which other slit could be uncovered so that the screen would be completely dark at point X? Explain.

Suppose that this *pair* of slits is uncovered, so that point X is completely dark. If slit 2 were now uncovered, would point X remain completely dark? If not, which other slit could also be uncovered (to pair with slit 2) so that point X once again becomes completely dark? Explain.

D. Show how you could group all ten slits into five pairs of slits so that the light waves from each pair add to zero at point *X*.

E. Suppose that the number of slits is doubled and the distance between adjacent slits is halved. (See below.) The new slits are labeled *1a–10a*. (The diagram uses the same scale as the preceding one.)

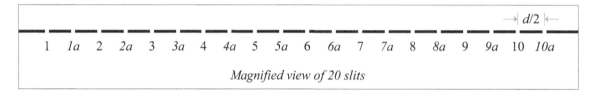

Magnified view of 20 slits

Would the first minimum in this case be located at the same angle θ as in part B? Explain.

F. If we continued to add slits in this way (*i.e.*, doubling the number of slits, but halving the distance between adjacent slits), would the angle to the first minimum change? Explain.

When the number of slits becomes very large as shown below, how can the slits be paired to determine the angle to the first minimum?

Magnified view of many, many slits

II. Motivation for a model for single-slit diffraction

The photograph below illustrates the pattern that appears on a distant screen when light from a distant point source passes through a single narrow vertical slit. This pattern is an example of a *single-slit diffraction pattern*.

A. How is this pattern *different* from what you would predict using the ideas developed in geometrical optics (*e.g.*, light travels in straight lines through slits)?

The presence of minima in a diffraction pattern suggests that diffraction is an interference phenomenon. We can model single-slit diffraction as follows: Consider the slit as consisting of many identical, very narrow, evenly-spaced "slits" that are so close to one another that the edges of these "slits" meet. The interference pattern produced by the light passing through the many "slits" approximates the single-slit diffraction pattern.

B. Consider the following dialogue:

Student 1: "I don't see why there are minima when there's only a single slit—I think you need two waves to have destructive interference."

Student 2: "You can model the single slit as many identical smaller interfering 'slits,' each small enough to act like a point source. The first minimum occurs where the path length difference from the two 'slits' at the edges of the single slit is $\lambda/2$."

Do you agree with student 2's response to student 1? Discuss your reasoning with your partners.

III. Applications of the model

A. The photograph at right shows the diffraction pattern produced on a distant screen by green light incident on a narrow slit.

Use an "×" to mark the locations that correspond to the first minima.

Which locations correspond to higher-order minima?

Suppose that red light, instead of green light, were incident on the same slit.

Determine whether the angle to the first minimum for red light would be *greater than, less than,* or *equal to* that for green light. In the space below, draw diagrams that support your prediction, and explain your reasoning.

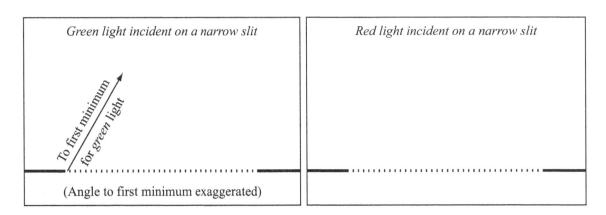

Green light incident on a narrow slit

To first minimum for green light

(Angle to first minimum exaggerated)

Red light incident on a narrow slit

Would you expect the locations of the higher-order minima to change? If so, how?

In the space below the photograph at the top of the page, show how the diffraction pattern would be different if red light, rather than green light, were incident on the narrow slit.

Obtain a color photograph that shows the diffraction patterns produced by red light and by green light on a narrow slit so that you may check your predictions.

⇨ Discuss your answers with a tutorial instructor.

Tutorials in Introductory Physics
McDermott, Shaffer, and the P.E.G., U. Wash.

©Pearson
Custom 2nd Ed., for U.CO, Boulder

B. The photograph at right shows the diffraction pattern produced by laser light incident on a narrow slit.

Pattern due to narrow slit

Use the model that we have developed to predict how the pattern would change if the slit were made *even narrower*. Explain your reasoning and sketch your prediction in the space provided at right.

Pattern due to even narrower slit

Ask a tutorial instructor for the photograph showing diffraction patterns produced by light incident on a narrow slit and on an even narrower slit so that you may check your predictions.

C. Describe what you would see on the screen if the width of the slit were gradually decreased to zero. Discuss your predictions with your partners.

D. If a diffraction pattern has several minima (like the patterns shown in this tutorial), is the width of the slit *greater than, less than,* or *equal to* λ? Explain your reasoning.

E. In part A, you drew a diagram that showed how to find the angle to the first minimum for green light incident on a narrow slit. Use your diagram to determine whether the width of the slit was *greater than*, *less than*, or *equal to* the wavelength of the incident light in that case.

Is this comparison consistent with your answer to part D? If not, resolve the inconsistency.

F. Use the model that we have developed to write an equation that can be used to determine the angle to the first minimum in the case of single-slit diffraction with a slit of width *a*.

Explain how you can account for the fact that the above equation, which describes the location of a minimum in the case of single-slit diffraction, is similar in appearance to the equation that describes the location of a maximum in the case of two-source interference.

I. Single-slit diffraction

Monochromatic light from a distant point source is incident on a mask that contains a single narrow vertical slit. The photograph at right shows the pattern produced on a distant semicircular screen. The corresponding graph of relative intensity is shown above the photograph, where *relative intensity* is intensity divided by the maximum intensity [*i.e.*, $I(\theta)/I_{max}$].

θ (radians)

Pattern on screen due to *single* slit

A. The minima that occur in the case of a single slit are called *diffraction minima*. On the photograph and on the graph, identify the locations of the diffraction minima.

B. Consider the following dispute between two physics students:

Student 1: "In lab, I determined that the width of one of the slits that we used to study single-slit diffraction was about 0.1 mm—that's definitely larger than λ."

Student 2: "You must have made a mistake. A diffraction pattern has minima only when the slit width is less than λ."

Do you agree or disagree with each of these students? Explain your reasoning.

II. Combined interference and diffraction

A. A second slit, identical in size to the first, is cut in the mask. The distance between the centers of the slits, *d*, is equal to 50λ.

What would you see on the screen if the original slit were covered and the second slit were uncovered?

B. Both slits are now uncovered.

For what angles will the light from each point on one slit be 180° out of phase with the light from the corresponding point on the other slit? (*Hint:* For small angles, $\sin \theta \approx \theta$, where θ is in radians.)

On the relative intensity graph above, clearly label these angles.

Tutorials in Introductory Physics
McDermott, Shaffer, and the P.E.G., U. Wash.

©Pearson
Custom 2nd Ed., for U.CO, Boulder

When the second slit is uncovered, will the intensity at the locations of the diffraction minima *increase, decrease,* or *stay the same?* Explain.

When the second slit is uncovered, how will the pattern on the screen change? In the space below the photograph on the previous page, clearly show how the pattern would be different.

⇨ Check your answers to part B with a tutorial instructor.

C. Suppose that the width of both slits, *a,* were gradually decreased (while keeping the distance between the centers of the slits the same).

Which minima would move as *a* is decreased?

Choose two or more relative intensity graphs below that illustrate such a change. (Enlargements of these graphs have also been provided.)

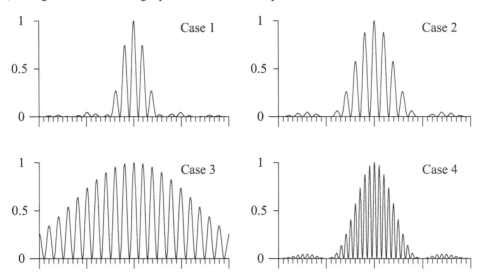

D. Suppose instead that the distance between the centers of the slits, *d,* were gradually decreased (while keeping the widths of the slits the same).

Which minima would move as *d* is decreased?

Choose two or more relative intensity graphs in part C above that illustrate such a change.

Tutorials in Introductory Physics
McDermott, Shaffer, and the P.E.G., U. Wash.

©Pearson
Custom 2nd Ed., for U.CO, Boulder

The minima that occur when only one slit is open are called diffraction minima. The minima that occur where the light from each point on one slit is 180° out of phase with the light from the corresponding point on the other slit are called *interference minima*.

E. The four relative intensity graphs from part C are reproduced below. In each case:

- Clearly label (1) the interference minima that are closest to the center of the pattern and (2) the diffraction minima that are closest to the center of the pattern.

- Sketch the graph of relative intensity that would result if one of the slits were covered.

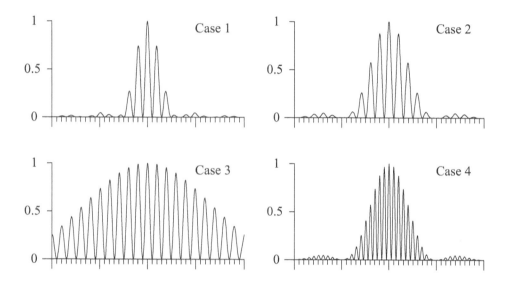

For each of the four cases, is your relative intensity graph consistent with the minima that you identified? If not, resolve any inconsistencies.

⇨ Check your answers to parts C–E with a tutorial instructor.

F. Consider the relative intensity graph shown at right.

Suppose that both slits were made narrower (without changing the distance between the centers of the slits).

On the graph at right, indicate how the relative intensity would change. Explain.

Suppose that after gradually narrowing both slits, one of the slits were then covered. On the axes provided, sketch the relative intensity graph for this case.

How does your graph compare to what you would expect for a *point source?* If it is different, how could you modify the physical situation so that the relative intensity graph better approximates that due to a point source?

In order for the relative intensity graph to be a good approximation of that due to a point source, how must the width of the slit compare to λ? Explain your reasoning.

III. Quantitative predictions

Consider the following relative intensity graph for a double-slit experiment. The wavelength of the light used was $\lambda = 633$ nm.

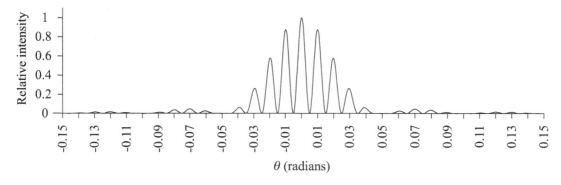

θ (radians)

A. Determine the width of the slits and the distance between the slits. Clearly indicate which features of the graph you are using.

Compare your results with those obtained by your partners. If your answers are different, resolve any discrepancies.

Tutorials in Introductory Physics
McDermott, Shaffer, and the P.E.G., U. Wash.

©Pearson
Custom 2nd Ed., for U.CO, Boulder

B. Consider the following comment made by a student:

"To determine slit width, I used the first minimum, at θ = 0.005 radians, and to determine the distance between the slits, I used the first maximum, at θ = 0.01 radians."

What is the flaw in the reasoning used by this student? Explain your reasoning.

C. You may have already noticed that the maxima are (approximately) 0.01 radians apart, except that there are no maxima at θ = 0.05 radians or θ = 0.10 radians.

How can you account for these "missing" maxima? (*Hint:* Consider how the relative intensity graph would be different if the width of the slits were decreased.)

Is your answer consistent with your response to part A in this section? If not, resolve the inconsistency.

I. Transmission and reflection at a boundary

The sketches below show a pulse approaching a boundary between two springs. In one case, the pulse approaches the boundary from the left; in the other, from the right. The springs are the same in both cases, and the linear mass density is greater for the spring on the right than for the spring on the left.

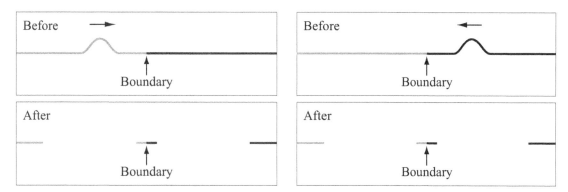

Complete the sketches to show the shape of the springs a short time after the trailing edge of the pulse shown has reached the boundary. Be sure to show correctly (1) the relative widths of the pulses and (2) which side of the spring that each pulse is on. (Ignore relative amplitudes.)

Compare your diagrams with those of your partners. Resolve any inconsistencies.

II. Thin-film interference

You may have observed that when a beam of light strikes a piece of glass, it is partially reflected and partially transmitted, similar to the behavior of a pulse on a spring when it reaches the junction between two connected springs.

In this tutorial, we consider a beam of light in air ($n = 1$) incident on a soap film ($n = {}^4/_3$). We make an analogy between this situation and a pulse incident on a boundary between two springs of different mass densities.

A. In this analogy, would the soap film better correspond to the spring with the larger linear mass density or to that with the smaller linear mass density? Explain your reasoning.

Discuss your reasoning with your partners.

B. When comparing two materials of different indices of refraction, the material with the higher index of refraction is sometimes said to be more "optically dense" than the other. Is this terminology consistent with the analogy that you made in part A?

Tutorials in Introductory Physics
McDermott, Shaffer, and the P.E.G., U. Wash.

©Pearson
Custom 2nd Ed., for U.CO, Boulder

C. Consider light incident on a *thin* soap film, as illustrated in the cross-sectional side-view diagram at right.

The soap film is supported by a loop (not shown), which is held vertically. Only a small portion of the film has been shown; the thickness of the film is greatly exaggerated.

In answering the following questions, use an analogy between this situation and the connected springs in parts A and B.

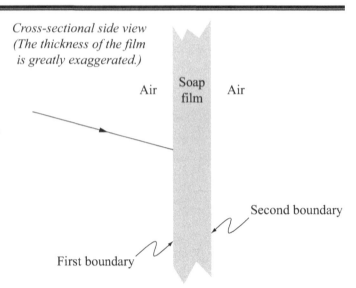

Cross-sectional side view (The thickness of the film is greatly exaggerated.)

Air

Soap film

Air

First boundary

Second boundary

1. Reflection and transmission at the first boundary

   a. On the diagram, draw rays that correspond to the light that is transmitted and reflected at the first boundary (on the left).

   b. Is the frequency of the transmitted wave (in the film) *greater than, less than,* or *equal to* the frequency of the incident wave (in the air)?

   c. Is the wavelength of the transmitted wave (in the film) *greater than, less than,* or *equal to* the wavelength of the incident wave (in the air)?

   d. For light incident on the first boundary, would the reflection at this boundary be more like that from a *fixed end* or that from a *free end?* Explain.

   e. On the basis of your answers above:

      At the first boundary, would the reflected wave be *in phase* or *180° out of phase* with the incident wave (*i.e.,* is there a phase change upon reflection)?

      At the first boundary, would the transmitted wave be *in phase* or *180° out of phase* with the incident wave (*i.e.,* is there a phase change upon transmission)?

Tutorials in Introductory Physics
McDermott, Shaffer, and the P.E.G., U. Wash.

©Pearson
Custom 2nd Ed., for U.CO, Boulder

2. Reflection at the second boundary

    a. Continue the transmitted ray (from part 1) through the film to the second boundary (on the right). Then draw rays that correspond to the light that is transmitted and reflected at the second boundary.

    b. For light incident on the second boundary, would the reflection at this boundary be more like that from a *fixed end* or that from a *free end?* Explain.

        At the second boundary, would the reflected wave be *in phase* or *180° out of phase* with the incident wave (in the film)?

3. Transmission at the first boundary

    Continue the reflected ray from part 2 through the film back to the first boundary. Then draw rays that correspond to the light that is transmitted and reflected at this boundary.

    Would there be a phase change on transmission at this boundary?

D. Light of frequency $f = 7.5 \times 10^{14}$ Hz is incident on the left side of the soap film.

    Determine the numerical values of the:

    • frequency of the wave in soap film (in Hz)

    • wavelength in air (in nm)

    • wavelength in film (in nm)

E. Suppose that an observer were located on the left side of the soap film in part C.

    Which of the rays that you drew could reach this observer?

    How would these rays be different if the light were incident at essentially normal incidence?

III. A film of non-uniform thickness

Cross-sectional side view (not to scale)

A soap film supported by a vertical loop has settled and is thinner at the top than at the bottom. Light of frequency $f = 7.5 \times 10^{14}$ Hz is incident on the film ($n = {}^4/_3$) at essentially normal incidence.

A. Observer A is looking at the part of the film that is 75 nm thick.

  Consider two reflected rays that reach observer A, similar to the rays that you identified in part E of section II.

  1. How much farther (in nm) does one of these rays travel than the other in reaching observer A?

  2. What is the phase difference between these rays? (Be sure to take into account the phase changes that you identified in part C of section II as well as any phase difference due to path length difference.)

  3. Is observer A looking at a region of *maximum brightness, minimum brightness,* or *neither?* Explain your reasoning.

B. Observer B is looking at the part of the film that is 150 nm thick.

  Is this observer looking at a region of *maximum brightness, minimum brightness,* or *neither?* Explain your reasoning.

Tutorials in Introductory Physics
McDermott, Shaffer, and the P.E.G., U. Wash.

©Pearson
Custom 2nd Ed., for U.CO, Boulder

C. Observer C is looking at the thinnest part of the film, where the film is *extremely* thin. To this observer, would the film appear *bright* or *dark?* Explain your reasoning.

D. Describe the appearance of the film as a whole.

⇨ Check your answers to parts A–D with a tutorial instructor.

E. What are the three smallest film thicknesses for which there would be maximum *constructive* interference?

What are the three smallest film thicknesses for which there would be maximum *destructive* interference?

F. The thickness of the film is 1650 nm at the bottom of the film, where the film is the thickest.

1. Would this part of the film appear *bright, dark,* or *in between?* Explain.

2. Suppose that the frequency of the incident light were increased.

   How, if at all, would the appearance of the thinnest part of the film change?

   Would the number of bright and dark regions *increase, decrease,* or *stay the same?* Explain your reasoning.

I. Polarization of light

A. Look at the room lights through one of the polarizing filters provided.

Describe how the filter affects what you see. Does rotating the filter have an effect?

B. Hold a second polarizing filter in front of the first, and look at the room lights again.

Describe how the filter affects the light that you see. How does rotating one of the filters with respect to the other affect what you see?

On the basis of your observations, why is it appropriate to use the term *filter* to describe these pieces of apparatus?

How is the behavior of the polarizing filters *different* from the behavior of colored acetate filters?

You have learned that light may be thought of as a wave consisting of oscillating electric and magnetic fields. If the electric field in all parts of a light beam oscillates along a single axis, the light beam is said to be *linearly polarized,* or simply, *polarized.* For example, the diagram at right represents a polarized light wave moving in the positive *x*-direction in which the electric field oscillates only along the *y*-axis. By convention, the direction along which the electric field oscillates (in this case, the *y*-direction) is called the *direction of polarization* of a light beam. If the electric field oscillates in different, random directions within the same light beam, that beam is said to be *unpolarized.*

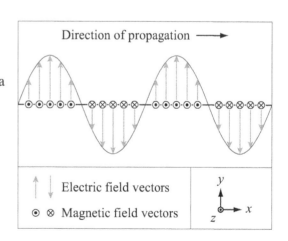

Direction of propagation →

↑ ↓ Electric field vectors

⊙ ⊗ Magnetic field vectors

Tutorials in Introductory Physics
McDermott, Shaffer, and the P.E.G., U. Wash.

©Pearson
Custom 2nd Ed., for U.CO, Boulder

II. Polarizing filters

The light transmitted by a polarizing filter (or *polarizer*) depends upon the relative orientation of

the polarizer and the electric field in the light wave. Every polarizer has a *direction of*

polarization, which is often marked by a line drawn on it. The electric field of the transmitted

wave is equal to the component of the electric field of the incident wave that is *parallel* to the

direction of polarization of the polarizer.

A. Do the room lights produce polarized light? Explain how you can tell from your observations.

B. Suppose that you had two marked polarizers (*i.e.,* their directions of polarization are marked).

Predict how you should orient the polarizers with respect to one another so that the light transmitted through the polarizers would have (1) *maximum* intensity or (2) *minimum* intensity. Discuss your reasoning with your partners and then check your predictions.

When two polarizers are oriented with respect to each other such that the light transmitted

through them has minimum intensity, the polarizers are said to be *crossed.*

C. Suppose that you had a polarizer with its direction of polarization marked. How could you use this polarizer to determine the direction of polarization of another (unmarked) polarizer? Explain your reasoning.

D. A beam of light is incident on a polarizer, as shown in the side-view diagram below. The direction of polarization of the light makes an angle θ with respect to the polarizer's direction of polarization. (See front-view diagram.) The amplitude of the electric field of the incident light is E_o. The magnetic field (not shown) has an amplitude B_o.

Side view

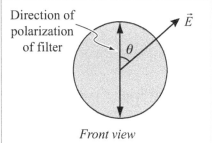

Front view

The vector $\vec{E}$ represents the electric field of the incident light at the front surface of the polarizer at a particular time. Resolve $\vec{E}$ into two components: one that is *transmitted* by the polarizer and one that is *absorbed* by the polarizer.

What is the *direction* of the electric field of the transmitted light? How, if at all, is it different from the direction of the electric field of the incident light? Explain.

Write an expression for the *amplitude* of the electric field of the transmitted light, in terms of E_o and θ.

Write an expression for the *amplitude* of the magnetic field of the transmitted light, in terms of B_o and θ. Explain your reasoning.

Write an expression for the *intensity* of the transmitted light in terms of I_o, the intensity of the incident light, and θ. Show all work. (*Hint:* If the amplitude of the electric field were reduced by a factor of two, by what factor would the intensity be reduced?)

⇨ Check your results from part D with a tutorial instructor.

E. An observer is looking at a light source through two polarizers as shown in the side-view diagram at right. The polarizers are crossed, that is, they are oriented so that the light transmitted through them has *minimum* intensity.

Crossed polarizers

1. Suppose that a third polarizer were inserted at the position marked *X*, shown above.

    Predict how, if at all, this change would affect the intensity of the light reaching the observer. Does your answer depend on the orientation of the third polarizer? Discuss your reasoning with your partners.

    Check your prediction experimentally. (Ask a tutorial instructor to show you the equipment that you need in order to do so.) If your prediction was incorrect, identify those parts of your prediction that were wrong.

    How can you apply your results from part D to help you account for your observations? Support your answer with one or more diagrams.

2. Suppose that instead a third polarizer were inserted at the position marked *Y*, shown above.

    Predict how, if at all, this change would affect the intensity of the light reaching the observer. Does your answer depend on the orientation of the third polarizer? Discuss your reasoning with your partners.

F. Consider a beam of *unpolarized* light that is incident on a polarizer. What is the intensity of the transmitted light in terms of I_o, the intensity of the incident light? (*Hint:* We can think of unpolarized light as equal amounts of light that are polarized *parallel* and *perpendicular* to the direction of polarization of the polarizer.)

Selected topics

I. Applying Newton's laws to liquids

A square container filled with water is at rest on a table as shown. Two imaginary boundaries that divide the water into three layers of equal volume have been drawn in the diagram. (No material barrier separates the layers.)

A. In the spaces provided, draw an extended free-body diagram for each layer. For any *contact* forces, indicate the surface on which the force is applied (*e.g.*, by placing the *tip* of the arrow that represents the force at that surface.)

   The label for each force should indicate: (1) the type of force, (2) the object on which the force is exerted, and (3) the object exerting the force.

B. Rank the *vertical* forces on your free-body diagrams according to magnitude, from largest to smallest. Explain how you determined your ranking.

   How does the weight of layer 1 compare to that of layer 3?

   A liquid in which equal volumes have equal weight regardless of depth (*i.e.*, the density does not vary) is referred to as *incompressible*.

   Assume that all liquids in this tutorial are incompressible.

Extended
free-body diagrams

Layer 1

Layer 2

Layer 3

C. Imagine that a small hole is opened in the container wall near the bottom of each layer.

   1. Predict what will happen to the water near each hole. Explain.

   2. Check your prediction by observing the demonstration. Record your observations. (A sketch may be helpful.)

      What do your observations suggest about: (1) the *existence* of horizontal forces on the three layers of water in part A? (2) the *relative magnitudes* of the horizontal forces on the three layers?

      If necessary, revise your free-body diagrams in part A so that they are consistent with your answers to part C.2.

II. Pressure and force

A. Recall the relationship between force and pressure. (Consult your textbook if necessary.) Below we will apply this relationship to the three layers from part I.

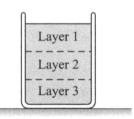

1. Which *force* would you use to determine the *pressure* at the bottom of layer 2? (There may be more than one correct answer.) Explain your reasoning. [*Hint:* Refer to your free-body diagrams from section I. Which force(s) are exerted at the bottom of layer 2?]

2. Which *area* would you use to determine the pressure at the bottom of layer 2? Explain.

3. Suppose instead that you wanted to determine the pressure at a point in the center of layer 2. For what object(s) would you draw a free-body diagram? Which force and which area would be useful in determining the pressure?

B. Suppose you wanted to determine the pressure at the top surface of layer 1. Which force would you use to determine this pressure? If necessary, modify your free-body diagrams to include this force. Be sure to label your diagram to indicate the object that exerts this force.

C. Consider points *L*, *M*, and *N* at the bottom of each of the layers.

Rank the points *L–N* according to pressure, from largest to smallest. Explain how your answer is consistent with your ranking of forces in section I.

The pressure *P* at a point in an incompressible liquid of density ρ is often described

mathematically as $P = P_o + \rho g h$, where P_o is atmospheric pressure.

D. Is your ranking in part C consistent with this equation? (*Hint:* At what point is $h = 0$? What is the pressure at that point?)

III. Pressure as a function of depth

The container at right is filled with water and is at rest on a table. An imaginary boundary that outlines a small volume of water has been drawn in the diagram. Treat this small volume of water as a single object.

A. Draw an extended free-body diagram for the small volume of water in the space below the figure.

B. Compare the magnitudes of the *horizontal* forces that you have drawn.

Extended free-body diagram for small volume of water

Is your answer consistent with the motion of the small volume of water? Explain.

C. Use your answer to part B to compare the pressures at points *T* and *U*. (*Hint:* How is the pressure at point *T* related to the force on the small volume of water by the water to its left?)

D. Rank the points *Q*–*U* according to pressure, from largest to smallest. Explain.

E. Consider the following student dialogue:

Student 1: "The pressure at a point is equal to the weight of the water above divided by the area. Therefore the pressure at point R is greater than the pressure at point S because there's no water above point S."

Student 2: "I agree. The pressure is $P_o + \rho g h$, and h is zero for point S and greater than zero for point R. Therefore, the pressure at R must be greater."

Do you agree with either student? Explain your reasoning.

⇨ Discuss your reasoning with a tutorial instructor.

IV. Pressure in a U-tube

A U-shaped tube is filled with water as shown.

A. Rank the points *A–F* according to pressure, from largest to smallest. Explain.

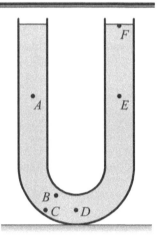

Is your ranking consistent with the equation $P = P_o + \rho g h$? If not, resolve the inconsistency.

B. The right end of the tube is now sealed with a stopper. The water levels on both sides remain the same. There is no air between the stopper and the water surface.

1. Does the pressure at points *A* and *D* *increase, decrease,* or *remain the same?* Explain.

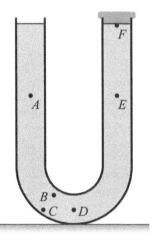

2. Is the pressure at point *E* *greater than, less than,* or *equal to* the pressure at point *D?*

    Does ΔP_{DE}, the difference in pressure between points *D* and *E*, change when the stopper is added? Explain.

3. Is the pressure at point *F* *greater than, less than,* or *equal to* atmospheric pressure?

    Is the force exerted by the stopper on the water surface on the right *greater than, less than,* or *equal to* the force exerted by the atmosphere on the water surface on the left?

C. A syringe is used to remove some water from the left side of the U-tube. It is observed that the water level on the left side is lowered, but the water level on the right does not change.

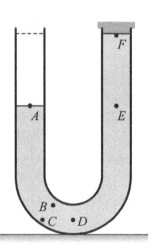

Consider the following student dialogue:

Student 1: "The pressure at point F must now be higher than atmospheric pressure because the water there is being pushed up against the stopper."

Student 2: "I think that the pressure at point E must be the same as at point A because they are at the same level. These points are both at atmospheric pressure. So the pressure at point F is lower than atmospheric pressure because we know that pressure gets less as you go up."

Student 3: "But water is more dense than air so the pressure at F cannot be less than atmospheric pressure."

With which student(s), if any, do you agree?

Tutorials in Introductory Physics
McDermott, Shaffer, and the P.E.G., U. Wash.

©Pearson
Custom 2nd Ed., for U.CO, Boulder

I. Buoyant force

A. A cubical block is observed to float in a beaker of water. The block is then held near the center of the beaker as shown and released.

1. Describe the motion of the block after it is released.

2. In the space provided, draw an extended free-body diagram for the block at the instant that it is released. Show the forces that the water exerts on each of the surfaces of the block separately.

   Make sure the label for each force indicates:

   - the type of force,

   - the object on which the force is exerted, and

   - the object exerting the force.

Extended free-body diagram
for block at instant it is released

3. Rank the magnitudes of the vertical forces in your free-body diagram. If you cannot completely rank the forces, explain why you cannot.

   Did you use the relationship between pressure and depth to compare the magnitudes of any of the vertical forces? If so, how?

   Did you use information about the motion of the block to compare the magnitudes of any of the vertical forces? If so, how?

4. In the box at right, draw an arrow to represent the vector sum of the forces exerted on the block by the surrounding water. How did you determine the direction?

   Sum of forces
   on block by water

   Is this vector sum the *net force* on the block? (Recall that the net force is defined as the vector sum of *all* forces acting on an object.)

   Is the magnitude of the sum of the forces exerted on the block by the water *greater than*, *less than*, or *equal to* the weight of the block? Explain.

Tutorials in Introductory Physics
McDermott, Shaffer, and the P.E.G., U. Wash.

©Pearson
Custom 2nd Ed., for U.CO, Boulder

B. The experiment is repeated with a second block that has the same volume and shape as the original block. However, this block is observed to sink in water.

1. In the space provided, draw an extended free-body diagram for the block at the instant it is released. As before, draw the forces exerted on each surface of the block by the water.

2. Compare the free-body diagram for the block that sinks to the one you drew in part A for the block that floats.

Which forces are the same in magnitude and which are different? (*Hint:* How does the pressure at each surface of this block compare to the pressure at the corresponding surface of the block in part A?)

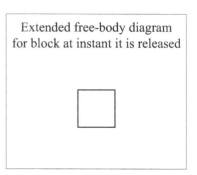

Extended free-body diagram
for block at instant it is released

Do any forces appear on one diagram but not on the other?

3. In the space provided, draw an arrow to represent the vector sum of the forces exerted on the block by the water.

How does this vector compare to the one you drew for the block that floats? (Consider both magnitude and direction.)

Sum of forces
on block by water

C. Imagine that you were to release the block from part B at a much greater depth. State whether each of the following forces on the block would be *greater than*, *less than*, or *equal to* the corresponding force on the block in part B above:

1. the upward force on the bottom surface on the block.

2. the downward force on the top surface of the block.

3. the vector sum of the forces on the block by the surrounding water. (*Hint:* Does the difference between the pressures at the top and bottom surfaces of the block change?)

The vector sum of the forces exerted on an object by a surrounding liquid is called the

buoyant force. This force is customarily represented by a single arrow on a free-body diagram.

D. In general, does the buoyant force on an object that is completely submerged in an incompressible liquid depend on:

  • the *mass* or *weight* of the object?

  • the *depth* below the surface at which the object is located?

  • the *volume* of the object?

⇨ Check your answers with a tutorial instructor before continuing.

II. Displaced volume

Consider two blocks of the same size and shape: one made of aluminum; the other, of brass. Both blocks sink in water. The aluminum block is placed in a graduated cylinder containing water. The volume reading increases by 3 mL.

A. By how much does the volume reading increase when the brass block is placed in the cylinder? (Assume that no water leaves the cylinder.) Explain.

When an object is placed in a graduated cylinder of liquid, the increase in the volume reading is called the *volume of liquid displaced* by the object.

B. Does the volume of water displaced by a *completely submerged* object depend on

  • the *mass* or *weight* of the object?

  • the *depth* below the surface at which the object is located?

  • the *volume* of the object?

  • the *shape* of the object?

III. Archimedes' principle

According to *Archimedes' principle*, the magnitude of the buoyant force exerted on an object by a liquid is equal to the weight of the volume of that liquid displaced by the object.

Consider the following statement made by a student:

"Archimedes' principle simply means that the weight of the water displaced by an object is equal to the weight of the object itself."

Do you agree with the student? Explain.

IV. Sinking and floating

A. A rectangular block, A, is released from rest at the center of a beaker of water. The block accelerates upward.

1. At the instant it is released, is the buoyant force on block A *greater than*, *less than*, or *equal to* its weight? Explain.

2. When block A reaches the surface, it is observed to float at rest as shown. In this final position, is the buoyant force on the block *greater than*, *less than*, or *equal to* the weight of the block? (*Hint:* What is the net force on the object?)

3. Are your answers to the questions above consistent with Archimedes' principle? (*Hint:* How does the volume of water displaced when the block is floating compare to that displaced when it was completely submerged?)

B. A second block, B, of the same size and shape as A but slightly greater mass is released from rest at the center of the beaker. The final position of this block is shown at right.

How does the buoyant force on block B compare to the buoyant force on block A:

• at the instant they are released? Explain.

• at their final positions? Explain.

C. A third block, C, of the same size and shape as A and B but with slightly greater mass than block B is released from rest at the center of the beaker. Two students predict the final position of the block and draw the sketch at right.

Student drawing

Student 1: "Since this block is heavier than block B, it will not go up as high after it is released, as shown at right."

Student 2: "Yes, I agree, the buoyant force is slightly less than the weight of this block, so it should come to rest a bit below the surface."

Explain what is *wrong* with each statement and with the diagram.

Tutorials in Introductory Physics
McDermott, Shaffer, and the P.E.G., U. Wash.

©Pearson
Custom 2nd Ed., for U.CO, Boulder

I. Pressure

A cylinder contains an ideal gas that is at room temperature. The cylinder is sealed with a piston of mass M and cross-sectional area A that is free to move up or down without friction. No gas can enter or leave the cylinder. The piston is at rest. Atmospheric pressure (*i.e.*, the pressure of the air surrounding the cylinder) is P_o.

Movable piston

Ideal gas

Free-body diagram for piston

Direction of net force on piston

A. In the space provided, draw a free-body diagram for the piston. Make sure the label for each force indicates: (1) the type of force, (2) the object on which the force is exerted, and (3) the object exerting the force.

B. In the space provided, draw an arrow to indicate the direction of the net force on the piston. If the net force is zero, state so explicitly.

C. Is the force exerted on the piston by the gas *inside* the cylinder *greater than, less than,* or *equal to* the force exerted on the piston by the air *outside* the cylinder? Explain.

Write an equation that relates the magnitudes of the vertical forces on your free-body diagram. (*Hint:* How are these forces related to the net force?)

D. Is the pressure of the gas in the cylinder *greater than, less than,* or *equal to* atmospheric pressure? Explain.

Determine the value of the pressure of the gas in the cylinder in terms of the given quantities. (*Hint:* Which of the forces that act on the piston can you use to find the pressure of the gas?)

E. A second cylinder contains a different sample of ideal gas at room temperature, as shown at right. The two cylinders and their pistons are identical.

Is the pressure of the gas in the second cylinder *greater than, less than,* or *equal to* the pressure in the cylinder above? If you cannot tell, state so explicitly. Explain.

Ideal gas

Ideal gas

Original cylinder   Second cylinder

⇨ Discuss your answers with a tutorial instructor before you continue.

II. Pressure and temperature

A. A cylinder of the type described in section I contains a
fixed amount of gas. Initially, it is in thermal equilibrium
with an ice-water bath. The pressure, volume, and
temperature of the gas are P_i, V_i, and T_i, respectively.

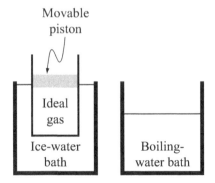

The cylinder is then removed from the ice water and
placed into boiling water. After the system has come to
thermal equilibrium with the boiling water, the pressure,
volume, and temperature are P_f, V_f, and T_f.

1. Is T_f *greater than*, *less than*, or *equal to* T_i?

2. Is P_f *greater than*, *less than*, or *equal to* P_i? Explain.

Is your answer consistent with your answer to part D of section I? If not, resolve any
inconsistencies.

3. Is V_f *greater than*, *less than*, or *equal to* V_i? Explain.

Is your answer consistent with the ideal gas law *(i.e., the relationship $PV = nRT$)?* If not,
resolve any inconsistencies.

B. In the process that you considered in part A above, which of the quantities P, V, n, and T are
held constant and which are allowed to change? Explain how you can tell.

C. Consider the following student dialogue regarding the above experiment.

Student 1: "According to the ideal gas law, the pressure is proportional to the temperature.
Since the temperature of the gas increased, the pressure must go up."

Student 2: "That's right. Since no gas entered or left the system, the volume did not
change. So the pressure must have increased."

Do you agree with either of the students? Explain your reasoning.

⇨ Check your reasoning with a tutorial instructor before you continue.

III. *PV* diagrams

Ideal gas processes are often represented graphically. For instance, a *PV diagram* is a graph of pressure *versus* volume for a given sample of gas. A single point on the graph represents simultaneously measured values of pressure and volume. These values define a *state* of the gas. We will use the convention that the origin [*i.e.*, (0, 0)] is the point where the axes intersect.

A. Sketch the process described in section II on the *PV* diagram provided. Label the initial and final states of the gas.

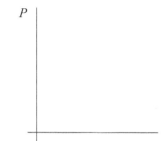

   Is your sketch consistent with your answer in part B of section II? Explain.

B. The same sample of ideal gas is used for a new experiment. The pressure and volume of the gas are measured at several times during the experiment. The values of *P* and *V* are recorded on the diagram shown at right.

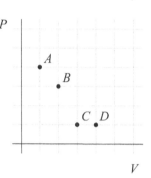

   1. Rank states *A–D* according to the temperature of the gas, from largest to smallest. If any two temperatures are the same, state so explicitly.

   2. Is your ranking consistent with the ideal gas law? If not, resolve the inconsistency.

   3. Is it possible for the gas to be in a state in which it has the same volume as in state *B* and the same temperature as in state *A?* If so, mark the location of the state on the *PV* diagram. If not, explain why not.

⇨ Check your reasoning with a tutorial instructor before you continue.

IV. Avogadro's number

A. Two identical cylinders and two identical pistons of the type described above contain hydrogen and oxygen, respectively. Both cylinders have been in the same room for a long time. Their pistons are at the same height.

   1. Compare the volumes of the gases in the two cylinders. Explain.

   Hydrogen   Oxygen

   2. Compare the temperatures of the gases in the two cylinders. Explain.

   3. Compare the pressures in the two cylinders. Explain.

   4. Compare the number of moles in the two cylinders. Explain.

   Is your answer consistent with the ideal gas law? If not, resolve the inconsistency.

B. A student looks up the molar masses and finds the values 2 g (for H_2) and 32 g (for O_2).

   1. Give an *interpretation* of these two numbers. (*Note:* A formula is not considered an interpretation.)

   2. Compare the masses of the gas samples in the two containers. Explain.

C. Consider the following student discussion regarding the cylinders described above.

   Student 1: "Since hydrogen molecules are so much smaller than oxygen molecules, there should be more of them in the same volume."

   Student 2: "No, since n = 2 for hydrogen, and n = 32 for oxygen, there must be more oxygen molecules."

   Find the flaws in the statements of both students. Explain.

I. Work

A. Recall the definition of work done on an object by an agent that exerts a force on that object. (You may wish to consult your textbook.)

In the spaces provided, sketch arrows to represent (1) a force exerted on an object and (2) the displacement of that object for cases in which the work done by the agent is:

Positive	Negative	Zero

In each case, does your sketch represent the *only* possible relative directions of the force and displacement vectors? If so, explain. If not, sketch at least one other possible set of vectors.

B. A block is pushed by a hand as it moves from the bottom to the top of a frictionless incline. The block is *speeding up* at a constant rate.

Frictionless incline

1. In the space provided, draw a free-body diagram for the block. Make sure the label for each force indicates: (1) the type of force, (2) the object on which the force is exerted, and (3) the object exerting the force.

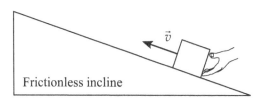

Free-body diagram for block

2. In the space provided, draw an arrow to show the direction of the net force on the block.

Net force on block

3. State whether the following quantities are *positive, negative,* or *zero.* In each case, explain your reasoning.

   • the work done on the block by the *hand*

   • the work done on the block by the *Earth*

   • the work done on the block by the *incline*

4. Is there work done on the hand by the block during this motion? If so, is this work *positive, negative,* or *zero?* Explain.

5. The principle of conservation of energy can be expressed in mechanics as $W_{net\ ext} = \Delta E_{tot}$. Explain how your answers to part 3 are consistent with this principle. (*Hint:* The *net work* on an object is the sum of the works done by all forces exerted on that object.)

6. Which, if any, of your answers in part 3 would be different if the block were being pushed up the incline with constant speed?

Describe the net work done on the block in that case.

C. An ideal gas is contained in a cylinder that is fixed in place. The cylinder is closed by a piston, as shown in the diagram at right. There is no friction between the piston and the cylinder walls.

1. Describe the direction of the force that the piston exerts on the gas.

Does your answer depend on whether the piston is moving?

2. How could the piston move so that the work it does on the gas is:

   • positive?

   • negative?

   Do your answers depend on your choice of coordinate system?

3. In each of the two cases in part 2, is there work done on the piston by the gas? If so, how is that work related to the work done on the gas by the piston? (Consider both sign and absolute value.)

⇨ Check your answers with a tutorial instructor before you continue.

II. Work and internal energy

A. Imagine that the cylinder from section I is thermally isolated from its surroundings by placing it in an insulating jacket. The piston is pressed inward to the position shown at right. We will refer to this compression as process 1.

Insulating jacket

Is the work done on the gas by the piston *positive, negative,* or *zero?*

Tutorials in Introductory Physics
McDermott, Shaffer, and the P.E.G., U. Wash.

©Pearson
Custom 2nd Ed., for U.CO, Boulder

In thermal physics, we are often interested in the *internal energy* (E_{int}) of a system. The internal energy of an ideal gas is proportional to the temperature and the number of moles of the gas. The internal energy can change when energy is exchanged with the system's environment (*e.g.*, objects that are outside the system of interest). The case above is one in which the internal energy of a gas changes due to work done on the gas (the system) by the piston (an agent external to the system). When such a system is thermally isolated, the change in internal energy of the system is equal to the net work done on it:

$$\Delta E_{int} = W_{\text{on system}} \qquad \text{(for a thermally isolated system)}$$

B. Does the internal energy of a gas in an insulated cylinder *increase, decrease,* or *remain the same* when the piston is pushed inward? Explain.

Does the temperature of the gas change? Explain.

C. Two students are discussing process 1 (see part A):

Student 1: "The volume of the gas decreases, but the pressure increases. Therefore, by the ideal gas law, the temperature must remain the same."

Student 2: "I disagree. The volume is less, and therefore the particles collide more often with one another, so the temperature must go up."

Neither student is correct. Find the flaws in the reasoning of each student. Explain.

⇨ Check your reasoning with a tutorial instructor before you continue.

III. Heat

A. Imagine that the cylinder from section II is no longer insulated, and the piston is locked in place. The gas is initially at room temperature.

The cylinder is then placed into boiling water and reaches thermal equilibrium with the water. We refer to this process as process 2.

1. In process 2, do the following quantities *increase, decrease,* or *remain the same?* Explain.

   • the temperature of the gas

   • the internal energy of the gas

   • the pressure of the gas

   • the volume of the gas

2. Sketch process 2 on the *PV* diagram at right.

3. Is there any work done on the gas in process 2? Explain. Is your answer consistent with your *PV* diagram?

The energy transfer that takes place in this process is called *heat transfer*. In this process, if the heat transfer to the gas *(Q)* is positive, the internal energy of the gas will increase.

B. In process 2, is the heat transfer to the gas *positive, negative, or zero?* Explain.

C. In process 2, is the heat transfer to the boiling water *positive, negative, or zero?* Explain.

IV. Heat, work, and internal energy

The *first law of thermodynamics* states that the change in internal energy of a closed system is equal to the sum of the heat transferred to the system and the net work done on the system:

$$\Delta E_{int} = Q + W_{\text{on system}}$$

A. Explain how you could write this law in terms of the work done *by* the system on its environment.

How does your textbook express the first law of thermodynamics?

B. In process 1 (section II) you did not need to consider heat transfer. What feature of the experiment prevented heat transfer to the gas?

C. In process 2 (section III) you did not need to consider work. What feature of the experiment prevented work from being done on the gas?

⇨ Check your reasoning with a tutorial instructor before you continue.

D. The cylinder, with the piston still locked in place, is now immersed in a mixture of ice and water and allowed to come to thermal equilibrium with the mixture.

The piston is then moved inward very slowly, in such a way that the gas is always in thermal equilibrium with the ice-water mixture. We will refer to this slow compression of the gas as process 3.

1. In process 3, do the following quantities *increase, decrease,* or *remain the same?* Explain.

   • the volume of the gas

   • the temperature of the gas

   • the internal energy of the gas

   • the pressure of the gas

2. Sketch process 3 on the *PV* diagram provided.

3. Determine whether the following quantities are *positive, negative,* or *zero:*

   • the work done on the gas in process 3 (explain your reasoning by referring to a force and a displacement)

   • the heat transfer to the gas in process 3

4. Are your answers above consistent with the first law of thermodynamics? Explain.

E. How does the compression in process 3 differ from the compression in process 1? Explain.

F. A student is considering process 3:

   "The temperature doesn't change; it is an isothermal process. Therefore, the heat transfer must be zero."

   Do you agree with this student? Explain.

I. Heat engines

A heat engine is a device that does work by extracting energy from its environment in the form of heat. All heat engines operate in cycles during which a system, also known as the working substance, passes through a series of thermodynamic processes returning repeatedly to each state.

A. The diagram at right represents a heat engine operating between reservoirs at 800 K and 400 K. The numbers and arrows indicate heat transfer to the system or work done on the system during each cycle.

1. How much work is done on the system during each cycle? Be sure to indicate whether it is positive or negative.

$$W_{\text{on sys}} =$$

2. How much heat is transferred to the system from the high temperature reservoir during each cycle? Be sure to indicate whether it is positive or negative.

$$Q_{\text{H (to sys)}} =$$

3. How much heat is transferred to the system from the low temperature reservoir during each cycle? Be sure to indicate whether it is positive or negative.

$$Q_{\text{L (to sys)}} =$$

4. The first law of thermodynamics can be written as $\Delta E_{\text{int}} = \Sigma Q_{\text{to sys}} + \Sigma W_{\text{on sys}}$. Use it to find the change in internal energy of the system during each cycle. Show your work.

Is your result consistent with the idea that energy is a state function? Explain.

B. The diagram at right represents a proposed cyclic device that operates between reservoirs at 600 K and 400 K.

Does this device satisfy the first law of thermodynamics? Explain.

Tutorials in Introductory Physics
McDermott, Shaffer, and the P.E.G., U. Wash.

©Pearson
Custom 2nd Ed., for U.CO, Boulder

II. The second law of thermodynamics

Not all processes that satisfy the first law of thermodynamics can occur. The *second law of thermodynamics* helps identify processes that do occur. It can be expressed in many equivalent ways. One expression, known as the entropy inequality, says $\Delta S_{int} \geq \Sigma\,(Q_{\text{to sys}}/T_{\text{env}})$ where S_{int} is a property of the system called entropy. Entropy, like energy, is a function of state.

A. The device discussed on the previous page is shown at right.

   1. Is the quantity $Q_{H\,\text{(to sys)}}/T_H$ *positive* or *negative?* What does it equal?

      $$Q_{H\,\text{(to sys)}}/T_H =$$

   2. Is the quantity $Q_{L\,\text{(to sys)}}/T_L$ *positive* or *negative?* What does it equal?

      $$Q_{L\,\text{(to sys)}}/T_L =$$

   3. What does the entropy inequality say about the minimum value of ΔS_{int}?

      $$\Delta S_{int} \geq$$

   4. Is your answer consistent with the idea that entropy is a state function and the assumption that the proposed device is cyclic? Explain

B. The Kelvin-Plank statement of the second law says, "No cyclic device can convert heat entirely into work." Is your answer from the previous question consistent with this statement?

Tutorials in Introductory Physics
McDermott, Shaffer, and the P.E.G., U. Wash.

©Pearson
Custom 2nd Ed., for U.CO, Boulder

The thermal efficiency of a heat engine, ε, is a measure of the amount of work done on the environment in each cycle for every Joule of heat transferred from the high temperature reservoir. Thus, it is defined as $\varepsilon = |W_{\text{on sys}}|/|Q_{\text{H (to sys)}}|$.

C. The proposed heat engine shown below operates between reservoirs at 800 K and 400 K. It may or may not be possible for this engine to function.

1. Calculate the thermal efficiency of the engine.

2. Does it satisfy the entropy inequality? Could it possibly function? Explain.

3. Two students discuss the proposed engine shown above.

Student 1: "This engine could work because heat is extracted from the hot reservoir in the form of energy to produce work. 300J = 500J - 200J."

Student 2: "I agree. By looking at efficiency we see that it would be 60%. This is a good efficiency but not impossible. There is no such thing as 100% efficiency."

Explain why you agree or disagree with the statement made by each student.

D. The engine shown below operates between reservoirs at 400 K and 300 K. The absolute value of the work it does during each cycle, labeled |X| in the diagram, is not specified.

1. Using the entropy inequality, find the maximum work |X| this engine could do during each cycle. Show your work.

2. What is the maximum thermal efficiency that this engine could have?

III. Carnot's theorem

A Carnot engine is an engine that operates with the *maximum possible* thermal efficiency. This thermal efficiency, called the Carnot efficiency, can be found using $\varepsilon_C = (T_H - T_L)/T_H$. Carnot's theorem, another expression of the second law of thermodynamics, says that no heat engine can have a thermal efficiency greater than that of a Carnot engine.

A. The engine discussed on the previous page is shown at right.

1. What is the efficiency of a Carnot engine operating between reservoirs at 400 K and 300 K? For what value of |X| is the engine shown to the right a Carnot engine?

2. How do these values compare to those you found on the previous page?

B. The proposed heat engine shown below operates between reservoirs at 500 K and 300 K. It may or may not be possible for this engine to function.

1. What is the thermal efficiency of this engine?

2. What is the thermal efficiency of a Carnot engine operating between reservoirs at 500 K and 300 K?

3. Two students discuss the proposed engine shown above.

   Student 1: "This engine is not a Carnot engine because it has a thermal efficiency that is not equal to the Carnot efficiency."

   Student 2: "I agree. And since we know that this engine is not a Carnot engine, it couldn't possibly function."

   In the space below, explain why you agree or disagree with the statement made by each student.

Tutorials in Introductory Physics
McDermott, Shaffer, and the P.E.G., U. Wash.

©Pearson
Custom 2nd Ed., for U.CO, Boulder

IV. Non-cyclic processes

A. The diagram at right shows a cylinder filled with an ideal gas sitting on a reservoir at 400 K. The cylinder is fitted with a piston that is free to move without friction when its path is not blocked by a pin.

The lower pin is removed allowing the gas to expand rapidly. During this process, 600 J of heat are transferred from the reservoir to the gas.

1. What can be said about the change in internal energy of the gas?

2. What can be said about the change in entropy of the gas?

B. Systems that cannot exchange energy in the form of heat or mechanical work with their surroundings are said to be isolated.

1. What can be said about the change in internal energy of an isolated system?

2. What can be said about the change in entropy of an isolated system?

I. Review of two-slit interference of light

Pattern on distant screen

Light of wavelength λ from a distant point source is incident on two very narrow slits, S_1 and S_2, a distance d apart. (See diagrams at right.) The photograph above right shows the pattern seen on a distant screen.

A. In the magnified view of the slits, an arrow is drawn showing the direction from slit S_1 to an arbitrary point on the screen, point X. On the magnified view:

- draw an arrow to indicate the approximate direction from slit S_2 to the *distant* point X.

- identify and label the line segment that represents the path length difference from the slits to point X.

For small angles θ (where θ is measured in radians), what is the approximate path length difference?

B. For what values of the path length difference (in terms of λ) will there be:

- maximum constructive interference *(i.e., a maximum)?*

- complete destructive interference *(i.e., a minimum)?*

C. Suppose that a *single* change were made to the apparatus (keeping the distance between the mask and the screen fixed), resulting in the new pattern shown.

Original pattern on screen

New pattern on screen

Center of screen

1. Are the angles to the interference maxima in the new pattern *greater than, less than,* or *equal to* those in the original pattern? Explain how you can tell from the photographs.

Tutorials in Introductory Physics
McDermott, Shaffer, and the P.E.G., U. Wash.

©Pearson
Custom 2nd Ed., for U.CO, Boulder

2. If the wavelength of light *(λ)* was the *only* quantity changed, determine (i) whether λ was *increased* or *decreased*, and (ii) whether it was changed by a factor that was *greater than*, *less than*, or *equal to* 2. Explain how you can use your results from parts A and B to justify your answer.

3. If the slit separation *(d)* was the *only* quantity changed, determine (i) whether *d* was *increased* or *decreased*, and (ii) whether it was changed by a factor that was *greater than*, *less than*, or *equal to* 2. Explain how you can use your results from parts A and B to justify your answer.

⇨ Check your reasoning with a tutorial instructor.

II. Two-slit interference of electrons

A beam of electrons is accelerated through a potential difference, *V*. The beam is incident on two narrow slits. The photograph shows the pattern seen on a phosphorescent screen placed far from the slits. (When an electron hits a small portion of the screen, that portion of the screen glows.)

A. Which is a better model for how the electrons behave in this case: that they propagate in straight lines through the slits, or that they propagate like waves? Explain how you can tell.

Pattern seen on screen

Top view (not to scale)

B. Suppose that the above experiment were repeated but with the electrons accelerated through a potential difference of 0.5*V* instead of *V*.

1. Predict whether the bright regions on the screen would *move closer together, move farther apart,* or *stay at the same locations*. Discuss your reasoning with your partners.

Obtain a figure that shows how the interference pattern would change if the accelerating voltage were halved so that you may check your prediction.

2. On the basis of the figure, would you conclude that halving the accelerating voltage changes the wavelength of the electron wave?

   If so: Does the wavelength increase or decrease?
   Does the wavelength change by a factor that is *greater than, less than,* or *equal to* 2? Explain how you can tell from the figures.

   If not: Explain how you can tell that the wavelength did not change.

3. How would *halving* the accelerating voltage affect each of the quantities listed below? In particular, determine (i) whether each quantity would *increase* or *decrease,* and (ii) whether each quantity would change by a factor that is *greater than, less than,* or *equal to* 2. Explain your reasoning in each case.

   • the kinetic energy of each electron that reaches the slits

   • the momentum of each electron that reaches the slits

   • the de Broglie wavelength of each electron that reaches the slits

4. Are your answers to parts 2 and 3 regarding the de Broglie wavelength of the electron consistent? If not, resolve any inconsistencies.

   Now that you have worked through parts 2 and 3, review your answer to part 1. Do you still agree with your earlier reasoning? If not, how would you revise it?

C. Suppose you were to perform the electron interference experiment described in part A.

Describe two independent methods that you could use in order to determine the de Broglie wavelength of the electrons. Include in your descriptions the measurements you would need to make and the steps you would need to follow in each case.

III. Application: Davisson-Germer experiment

Monoenergetic electrons are incident on a nickel crystal. It is observed that intense scattering occurs at angles θ according to the Bragg condition, $2d \sin\theta = n\lambda$. (See diagram at right.)

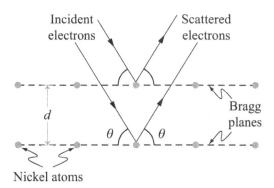

A. Use trigonometry to show that the path length difference between the two scattered beams shown is equal to $2d \sin\theta$. Show all work.

B. Suppose that this experiment were repeated, each time with a *single* change made to the apparatus. For each change below, determine whether each of the angles θ at which intense scattering occurs would become *larger, smaller,* or *stay the same*. Explain your reasoning in each case.

1. The kinetic energy of the incident electrons is decreased.

2. The electrons are replaced with neutrons, with each neutron having the same speed as each of the original electrons.

I. Introduction to the photoelectric effect experiment

The photoelectric effect apparatus below consists of two metal electrodes (A and B) inside a glass tube containing no air. A wire connects the electrodes as shown. Assume the electrodes are identical and initially uncharged.

Monochromatic light is directed toward electrode B. In this tutorial, the photoelectric effect will be considered using a model in which: Light is treated as consisting of particles called photons. Each incoming photon can be treated as interacting with only one electron in the metal; in the process, the photon imparts its energy to the electron.

A. An ammeter is used to measure the current in the circuit.

1. For the ammeter shown, conventional current from left to right results in a positive reading. Would the reading be *positive* or *negative* if the current were from right to left? Explain.

2. Sketch an ammeter in the circuit above. Orient the ammeter so that clockwise current results in a positive reading, and counterclockwise current results in a negative reading.

3. While the light is *off*, is the current *zero* or *non-zero?* Explain.

B. The light source is now *turned on.* It is observed that there is a *constant non-zero* current.

1. Do you think any electrons are crossing the gap between the electrodes? Explain.

2. If electrons are crossing the gap, do they move in the tube *from A to B* or *from B to A?*

3. Do electrons flow through the circuit *clockwise* or *counterclockwise?* Explain.

4. Does the direction of electron flow as determined in question 3 correspond to a positive reading on the ammeter or a negative one? Explain.

5. How could you alter the experiment to increase the current through the ammeter? Explain.

⇨ Discuss your answers to section I with a tutorial instructor before continuing.

II. Effect of changing the electrodes

Two sets of electrodes are shown below. The electrodes are not a part of a circuit. Identical light sources are *turned on* and directed toward electrode B in each case. Assume that the number of electrons that leave B is small compared to the total number of electrons in the metal.

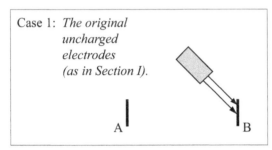

Case 1: *The original uncharged electrodes (as in Section I).*

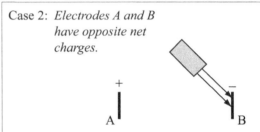

Case 2: *Electrodes A and B have opposite net charges.*

A. For each case above, sketch several possible paths of individual electrons leaving plate B. Ignore gravitational effects.

1. Clearly indicate whether each of these electrons reaches plate A.

2. What forces, if any, affect the motion of the electrons? Explain.

B. Is the number of electrons that leave electrode B in case 2 *greater than, less than, or equal to* the number that leave electrode B in case 1? Explain.

C. Is the number of electrons that reach electrode A in case 2 *greater than, less than, or equal to* the number that reach electrode A in case 1? Justify your reasoning.

D. In each case, is the kinetic energy of an electron as it reaches electrode A *greater than, less than, or equal to* its kinetic energy as it leaves electrode B? Explain.

E. In case 2, how could you alter the electrodes to increase the number of electrons that reach electrode A each second? Is there a maximum number that can reach A each second? Explain.

III. Effect of adding a battery

A. A 1.5V battery is added to the circuit as shown.

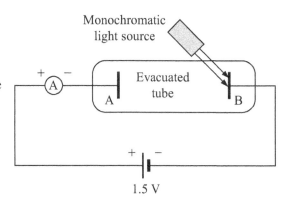

1. Label electrodes A and B according to the type of charge (+ or −) that accumulates.

2. When the light is *off*, is there a *constant non-zero* current through the ammeter? Explain.

B. Assume the light source is *on*.

1. Is the number of electrons emitted from electrode B each second when there is a battery in the circuit *greater than, less than, or equal to* the number emitted each second when there is no battery? Explain.

2. What is the voltage (*i.e.*, potential difference) across the electrodes ($\Delta V = V_A - V_B$)?

3. What does your answer to question 2 imply about whether the net charge on each of the electrodes changes? Explain.

4. Write an expression relating the potential difference ΔV to the change in kinetic energy of a single electron as it moves from electrode B to electrode A. (*Hint:* Consider the work done by the electric field between the electrodes or the potential energy associated with the field.)

⇨ Discuss your answers in section III with a tutorial instructor before continuing.

IV. Effect of varying the voltage across the electrodes

A. For the remainder of the tutorial, assume the light source is on. Let I_0 represent the ammeter reading with no battery in the circuit.

1. Is I_1, the current when there is one battery in the circuit, *greater than*, *less than* or *equal to* I_0? Explain. (*Hint:* Refer to part C of section II.)

2. A second battery is added in series with the first battery with the same orientation. Rank I_0, I_1, and I_2 (the current when there are two batteries in the circuit) according to magnitude, from largest to smallest. Explain.

3. Would inserting additional batteries continue to cause the current to increase? If so, is there a limit to the amount of current that can be produced? Explain.

4. Is it possible to use batteries to decrease the current? If so, show how to connect the batteries and sketch some possible paths of electrons.

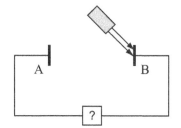

5. Could batteries be used to produce a constant clockwise flow of electrons (*i.e.*, a negative ammeter reading)? Justify your answer.

B. In the space at right, sketch an *I-V* graph for a photoelectric effect experiment. The relative currents for various voltages should be consistent with your answers in part A (*e.g.*, $I = I_o$ when $V = 0$ V); however, your graph need only be qualitatively correct. Complete the graph by imagining you can vary the voltage continuously by using a power supply.

Is there a particular point on the graph at which the current becomes zero? Explain.

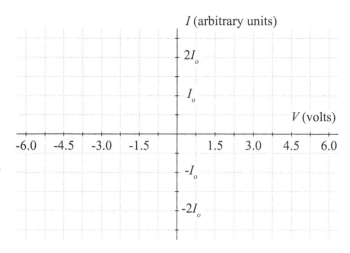

⇨ Discuss your answers to parts A and B with a tutorial instructor before continuing.

C. The voltage at which the current becomes zero is called the *stopping voltage, V_{stop}*.

   1. How can you account for the current becoming zero at the stopping voltage? Explain.

      (*Hint:* Draw paths of electrons that leave electrode B and indicate whether each of these electrons reaches electrode A.)

    A   B

   2. Consider a particular electron emitted from electrode B with the maximum possible kinetic energy and traveling directly to the left. How could you determine the kinetic energy of the emitted electron from the stopping voltage? Explain.

V. Work function

A. An experiment similar to the one in this tutorial is performed using incoming light of wavelength 175 nm. The stopping voltage is measured to be –2.8 V.

   1. What is the maximum possible kinetic energy of an electron emitted from electrode B?

   2. Calculate the energy of an incoming photon. (Recall that $h = 4.14 \times 10^{-15}$ eV-s.)

   3. Do your answers to questions 1 and 2 appear to be consistent with conservation of energy? Explain.

   4. Calculate the difference in the photon energy and the kinetic energy of the electron emitted from electrode B. This difference is referred to as the *work function*. How does the term "work" help explain the reason for the energy loss?

B. Obtain a chart of work functions for different metals from a tutorial instructor and use it to determine a possible material from which the electrodes in this experiment could be made.

Credits:

Page 119: Source: *Physics by Inquiry* by Lillian C. McDermott and the Physics Education Group. © 1996 by John Wiley & Sons, Inc. Reprinted by permission.

Page 120: Source: *Physics by Inquiry* by Lillian C. McDermott and the Physics Education Group. © 1996 by John Wiley & Sons, Inc. Reprinted by permission.

Page 155: Source: *Physics by Inquiry* by Lillian C. McDermott and the Physics Education Group. © 1996 by John Wiley & Sons, Inc. Reprinted by permission.

Page 162: Source: *PSSC Physics* by Uri Haber-Schaim, Judson B. Cross, John H. Dodge, and James A. Walter. © 1971 and 1976 by Education Development Center, Inc. Reprinted by permission.

Page 163: Source: *PSSC Physics* by Uri Haber-Schaim, Judson B. Cross, John H. Dodge, and James A. Walter. © 1971 and 1976 by Education Development Center, Inc. Reprinted by permission.

Page 164: Source: *PSSC Physics* by Uri Haber-Schaim, Judson B. Cross, John H. Dodge, and James A. Walter. © 1971 and 1976 by Education Development Center, Inc. Reprinted by permission.

Page 166: Source: *PSSC Physics* by Uri Haber-Schaim, Judson B. Cross, John H. Dodge, and James A. Walter. © 1971 and 1976 by Education Development Center, Inc. Reprinted by permission.

Page 168: Source: *PSSC Physics* by Uri Haber-Schaim, Judson B. Cross, John H. Dodge, and James A. Walter. © 1971 and 1976 by Education Development Center, Inc. Reprinted by permission.

Page 187: Source: *Physics by Inquiry* by Lillian C. McDermott and the Physics Education Group. © 1996 by John Wiley & Sons, Inc. Reprinted by permission.

Page 194: Source: K. Hendry, Seattle, Washington.

Page 199: Source: *Physics by Inquiry* by Lillian C. McDermott and the Physics Education Group. © 1996 by John Wiley & Sons, Inc. Reprinted by permission.

Page 200: Source: *Physics by Inquiry* by Lillian C. McDermott and the Physics Education Group. © 1996 by John Wiley & Sons, Inc. Reprinted by permission.

Page 206: Source: *Physics by Inquiry* by Lillian C. McDermott and the Physics Education Group. © 1996 by John Wiley & Sons, Inc. Reprinted by permission.